## We're All In
# THE FAMILY BUSINESS
### A Story About Faith, Work & Destiny

# *Doug Banister*

*and*
*Jeff Fray, John Secrest, and Steve Hall*

*"A refreshing story for everyone working in the trenches of the marketplace."*

*Published by William and Warren, Inc.*
*in conjunction with TFB Publishing*
*1200 Paint Rock Road*
*Kingston, Tennessee 37763*

*Library of Congress Cataloging-in-Publication Data*
*Banister, Doug;*
    *TFB Publishing*
    *ISBN 0-9652007-3-6*
    *1. Business Books*
    *2. Religious Fiction*

*Dewey System — Religion: Business*

*Cover design by Jonathan Longnecker, Knoxville, Tennessee*
*Cover photo of Doug Banister by Charles Garvey Photography, Knoxville, Tennessee*
*Text design by Debbie Patrick, Knoxville, Tennessee*
*Printed in the United States*

## THE FAMILY BUSINESS

Imagine the ideal family business. The business has been in your family for centuries. Your father has built the family business into a global powerhouse serving clients in every nation on earth. Thousands of people work for the family business in hundreds of different jobs. You are the father's beloved child. Long before you were born he dreamed of you joining him as a partner in the family business. He's been mentoring you for this role since you were a child. He knows what you are passionate about, what you fear, what you find life-giving and what deadens your soul. He sees you not just for who you are, but for who you will become. You are, to him, a person of destiny.

Knowing you better than you know yourself, your father has created the perfect place for you in the family business. His dream is coming true. His child is becoming his partner. Your dream is also coming true, too. You've longed to work for your father as long as you can remember. And now you are; partnering with him in a grand project that stretches across the centuries as well as the planet, serving with him in a job specially crafted just for you.

Steve Hall, Jeff Fray, John Secrest, Doug Banister
Good Friday
2004

**Family Business.** *(fam'le biz'nis) n.* **1.** The work of God in redeeming the world. **2.** God's work restoring a broken, twisted and distorted world to its original design. **3.** The project of bringing God's protection, leadership and blessing into all of life. **4.** Advancing the kingdom of God through work. **5.** Establishing God's dominion on earth.

# ONE

Brian was used to rushing around, so by the time he left the last session of the leadership-training seminar, he had already anticipated the series of moves necessary to put him at the departure gate by 6:35 pm, in time for his return flight. He had packed the night before and needed only to check out of his room before catching the shuttle to the airport. Hurrying through the lobby with his suitcase, briefcase, and tote bag he noticed flakes of wet, heavy snow beating in great succession against the gigantic picture window of the cozy retreat. His focus remained on the snow, weather that struck him as peculiar this early in fall, as he approached the front desk.

"Here you go Mr. Tucker," said the clerk as he pushed Brian's hotel bill across the dark wooden counter top. "Just sign at the bottom and you're all set."

"You don't think they will cancel flights, do you?" Brian asked, as he signed the bill.

"No sir, this is Denver. We're used to it," replied the clerk, almost with pride. "Go ahead and have a seat in the lobby and I'll call you when the shuttle arrives. It shouldn't be more than a few minutes."

Brian nodded, turned around and headed for a comfortable looking sofa near the great stone fireplace in the center of the lobby. Brian sank into the sofa, savoring an exhausting week well spent. Brian collected his thoughts as he sank into the chair. As hard as he tried, even with all the demands, Brian could not picture doing anything else in the world. He loved building things.

Brian was part of the management side of a rapidly growing construction company headquartered east of Nashville. Bright, passionate, and driven, Brian had so impressed his superiors that at the age of 35 he was being groomed to become the company vice president over operations. The company had invested heavily in Brian's future, and expected him to be a part of the team that would carry the them to "the next level" in the coming years.

Their belief in him came well-deserved; Brian gave it all he had, all the time. Though tired from a week of long days filled with intensive training sessions, Brian could not keep idle as he waited for the shuttle to arrive. He powered up his laptop, clicked on the "journal" file, and began to type.

*October 17th. Snowing pretty hard. Desk clerk says Denver International can handle it. This has been a tremendous week. The personality tests we took before coming out here really nailed me. The organizational 360 gave me good feedback – I was stung by a few low scores from the people who work for me. Need to think about that. Got a lot out of the session on situational leadership. Need to buy Blanchard's stuff when I get home. Would have saved a lot of headaches on the Savannah job had I known that. The company would have realized a greater profit, too.*

*I was the youngest guy in my breakout group*
*– most everybody else was in their forties or fifties –*
*top management from some pretty big companies.*
*Had two CEOs in my section. Maybe I'll be there*
*someday. I think I have a decent shot.*

Brian logged off and closed the computer. As the laptop whirred down, he moved deeper into the sofa. He had put on some hard miles over the last 15 years. He wondered if he could withstand what he would face in the next 15.

He had been with Vanguard Construction for the past six years, and had done well. Before that he was with a competitor out of Nashville where he had been noticed and hired away by the competition. His first job out of college, working for a young struggling engineering firm, gave him his first taste of success blended with hard work. It also established what friends and loved ones conceded as workaholism. Prior to joining the work-a-day world he was a dedicated business major, and a less than distinguished football walk-on at Auburn University. Aside from the divorce, life had treated him pretty well.

The years after the breakup were the worst ones of his life. His marriage started falling apart near the beginning of his ascent through the ranks at Vanguard. The timing created an odd symmetry; part of him felt successful and proven, but part him felt inadequate and exposed. Increasingly he felt like a fraud, a fake, sometimes even a performer. He resented his wife for leaving him, but her staying would've only served to remind him of his failure as a husband. With Deanna gone, he had only his job to give him meaning, and so to the job he gave his all.

But the job could only touch certain parts of his soul, and after a few years of languishing with an irreparably broken heart, he found love again; this time it was the love of God.

Loneliness had softened Brian enough to want a relationship again, even if he was less than certain of his ability to carry it through. While attempting to appear suitable to the young woman he had met at a Chamber of Commerce breakfast, he put on a coat and tie and escorted her to church. By the end of the service Brian had forgotten all about the girl and found himself in the front row praying with two older, peaceful-looking men. He considers that day the beginning of his spiritual journey.

Brian did faith as he did everything else: with gusto. He plunged ambitiously, but thoughtfully into his life in Christ. With each step came healing, and as each wound closed the hope of a more abundant life bloomed. And as Brian became more established in his church, he grew more aware of the needs there and more burdened to serve with his gifts, his money, and his time. He and his pastor had become close friends.

Recently, Pastor Russell had invited Brian to join the pastoral staff. Brian received the offer respectfully, even enthusiastically. He was proud of his church, a vibrant, diverse spiritual community that had a tremendous impact on hundreds of lives each year. Brian respected his pastor more than any man he knew – he was the real thing, a gifted leader with a servant's heart and not a whiff of ego about him. Yet somewhere deeper, Brian's heart recoiled. It seemed simple enough. He thought, "What better way to serve God than by being on staff at a church? On the other hand…"

On the other hand Brian loved his company, his work, his customers, even his subcontractors. (Usually). He didn't like how this new proposition felt deep inside. He felt spiritually cornered. A godly man, he was sure, would jump at the opportunity to serve on staff at his church. Yet Brian felt "called" to his work – could that be possible? The well-meaning pastor's offer created an internal tension he hated. On the flight to Denver for the seminar Brian had a startling realization: he loved his job. He also realized that he felt guilty for loving his job. While he wanted to serve God, he didn't want to leave his job. He began to suspect that somewhere along the way he had been taught to live in two worlds, a spiritual and a spatial, and this new offer exposed the deception. He anguished over having to make a decision but trusted that God did not make cruel demands. Somehow God would be faithful to speak if he would be faithful to listen. Of the few free moments he had on this trip, many were spent chewing on this problem.

As he stuffed the computer into his backpack, he prepared to still his mind and again take up a prayerful consideration of Pastor Russell's difficult offer. Before he could descend into a peaceful disposition, he felt a firm tap on the shoulder bring him back to the bustling hotel lobby.

"Mr. Tucker," the desk clerk muttered. "Mr. Tucker, sir. I just got a call from the shuttle driver. The airport closed. I'm sorry but you're snowed in here for at least tonight, and probably tomorrow. It's supposed to keep up like this for the next twenty-four hours. We have an arrangement with your airline when things like this happen, so don't worry about the bill. I have already checked you into the same room. I apologize for the inconvenience. I have been here 15 years," the clerk said a bit chagrined, "and the airport has only closed one other time for snow."

"I guess it's just not meant to be," Brian replied, oddly relieved. "There is a reason for everything."

# TWO

After settling back into his room, Brian became restless. He had spent most of the week in training sessions, only to spend his nights massaging budgets and catching up on e-mails in his room. These four walls were beginning to feel claustrophobic, so he decided to explore the rest of the cozy inn. Brian scanned a map of the hotel he found at the concierge desk. Hidden away down a long hallway on the second floor was a room called "The Study." "The Study" was exactly what the name implied, a warmly decorated room with walls lined with thousands of books. A burgundy leather sofa and two over-stuffed armchairs formed a semi-circle before a crackling fireplace. A service table was stocked with crackers, nuts, a hot water pot, a basket with a variety of teas and cocoas, and an electric coffee thermos labeled "HAZELNUT HOUSE BLEND." A heavy wooden table and chairs were nestled in the back of the room inviting serious students to spread out. The room smelled of wood, fire, and leather. Brian poured himself some coffee.

"Another prisoner I presume?"

Brian's eyes tried to adjust to the dim lights of the room. He noticed a man sitting in one of the stuffed chairs. A journal lay open on his lap. The man closed the journal quickly and slid it into his coat pocket. "I'm sorry?" Brian offered hoping the man would repeat the question.

"I said, 'Another prisoner, of the weather, the snow, I presume?'"

"Oh, yes. Looks like it."

The man put his book down and rose to shake Brian's hand. Brian recognized him from the seminar. He was Al Hunter, who had led the workshop on contract negotiation. A former Episcopal priest, Al had intrigued him. Al, or "Father Al" as the group liked to teasingly call him, was in his sixties, stocky but fit, built like a retired marine, with close-cropped gray hair and blue eyes that never looked away when you were talking. He had a tough but inviting face. He had been a priest for twenty years, then, during some kind of a spiritual crisis, he left the priesthood and went to work for his brother-in-law as a real estate developer. As it turned out, the priest had a knack for business and soon went out on his own and built a tremendously successful company. Now he divided his time between running his development company and growing his equally successful venture capital firm. His venture capital firm had birthed about twenty start-up companies. He sat on the boards of a dozen of them and seemed to manage a surprising number of relationships with young business leaders across the country. "My calling is to grow businesses," he had said earlier in the week, mingling, as Brian noticed, the language of the cloister with the language of the market.

Finding his seat and with a gesture of his hand offering Brian to join him, Al beamed at the cozy fire. "I suppose there are worse places to be snowed in," Al said smiling.

"I was just thinking the same thing," Brian replied as he nestled in. "I've needed some time to slow down, process things. The week was pretty hectic."

"They threw a lot at us, didn't they?"

Al had made a warm impression on Brian, and Brian found himself looking forward to this unexpected conversation. They sipped coffee and rehashed the conference as the fire burned down.

"What's your main takeaway?" Al asked.

"Actually, one of my takeaways I sort of brought with me. I am wrestling with something similar to what you described. What you said has really stuck with me."

"Oh, really? What was that? I say a lot of things. I sometimes talk too much!" Al joked. "What are you referring to?"

"Well," Brian began, "I'm referring to your faith, your spirituality, and how that relates to your work. I didn't expect that to come up here, and when it did, I guess it really resonated with me."

"Go on." Al leaned in. Both men could tell the conversation had moved from social superficiality to honest dialog.

"You were an Episcopal priest, right? And then you left the ministry and built businesses. You even said that 'business was your calling now.'"

"I did."

"I guess I am not used to people referring to their jobs like they are ministries." As he finished he could tell that his comment sounded condescending. He quickly added, "Oh, don't get me wrong. I'm not saying you're wrong to do that, in fact, what I mean to say is you've got me thinking about why people, lay people, don't see their jobs that way, like ministries."

"I understand," Al said. "It sounds awkward, maybe a little irreverent, even. But I can tell you this: I believe developing new businesses is more my vocation, my calling, than the priesthood was. I don't think I love God any less as a venture capitalist. Heck, I don't even think God loves me any less as a venture capitalist."

Brian told Al about his life, about being lost and then found, all of it: the divorce, the successes, the failures, and his love for his career. He ended with his current predicament, the offer to join the church staff made by Pastor Russell. Al understood that feeling of being torn among a church, a faith, a God you love, and a vocation, what some might simply call your job. Al had certainly been in his shoes.

"I live such a divided life," Brian continued. "I've tried everything I know to reconcile my two worlds. Instead of vacations I take mission trips. I serve at church. I give. I've even thought about going into full-time Christian ministry later, after I have made it on my own and can retire. I guess it just doesn't feel like it's enough in light of a pastoral position.... Maybe my pastor is right. Maybe God is asking me to sacrifice greatly, to deny myself. I don't think my pastor truly understands how much I love my work. He knows it has made me comfortable, financially. But I know that isn't what troubles me; money is no sacrifice for me, I live pretty simply. Maybe this is a test of faith, and if I really loved God I would leave my business for the ministry."

Al let Brian finish, knowing he needed to acknowledge the complexity of his feelings. He tried to encourage him, "Mission trips, tithing, serving; those are all important. So, what feels wrong about them?"

"It's not the activities themselves. It's like I said, they don't seem to be enough when asked to give...your vocation, livelihood. Being a manager for a construction firm seems so...so worldly, so..."

"...Seems so second-class?"

Brian paused for a moment and looked into the fire. "That sounds a little harsh when I hear you say it, but yes. When you are sitting with a pastor talking about the work of God, my work seems like a second-class way to spend life. I hate it, but I feel that way sometimes."

Brian thought for a moment. He was surprised he was allowing the depth of his feelings to rise during this conversation with a stranger, yet he didn't suppress anything, allowing even the subtle anger to surface. "A friend of mine said he was leaving his job for 'full-time Christian ministry.' He didn't come out and boast or preen, but you could tell he was proud of the 'sacrifice' he was making, and I'm sure he expected us, his friends, to be very impressed. When he told me I smiled and congratulated him, but deep down I was thinking, 'Does that mean I am a part-time Christian?'"

Al raised his eyebrows, as if to ask, "Does it?"

"A few weeks ago," Brian continued, leaning over the arm of his chair, assuring himself he had Al's complete attention, "I had lunch with a consultant working with my company. When he found out that I was interested in spiritual things, he said that while he made his living off of companies like ours, he gave a third of his consulting time 'to kingdom work.' I guess that means that what I do all day is not kingdom work." Al knew Brian was allowing himself, perhaps for the first time, to truly debate the issue with himself, so he let him keep talking.

Brian stopped for a moment fearing he was beginning to sound like a petty child, but no sooner had he leaned back than he started up again, as if he just needed to get this last thing off his chest. "Probably the most frustrating instance was during a conversation with my pastor. He's a great guy. I'd love to work with him. But our last conversation really bothered me. He said that the things I worked on in the construction business were all going to burn someday. Then he said that pastoral work invests in eternal things. Wouldn't I want to give my life to what really counts? He even described work as ultimately 'shuffling deck chairs on the Titanic.' Futile. Pointless, in the grand scheme of things."

Brian stared into the glowing embers of what remained of the fire. He was surprised and a little embarrassed by the intensity of his emotions. He never talked to anyone with this much freedom and honesty. He was a bit surprised to realize how deeply bothered he was by this issue, yet it felt good to talk about it. Brian looked tentatively at Al. After all, he barely knew the man. For a moment he wondered if the older man would lecture him for his selfishness. Brian's face felt warm. He felt flush with shame. The two sat in silence. Finally, Brian asked, "I didn't mean to get so self-righteous, but honestly Al, can you relate to any of this?"

"Yes," Al said. "I certainly can."

# THREE

Al rose and walked over to one of the bookshelves and began scanning the titles. After a few minutes his finger landed on a book and stopped. He pulled it off the shelf and started back for his chair, holding the book in front of him.

"You ever read this?" he asked, extending the copy of The Collected Works of Plato.

"Plato? Oh yeah, all the time. I have a copy in my bathroom," Brian quipped.

"Even if you've never read Plato you've been influenced by him, I guarantee it," Al replied. "In fact, Plato is partially responsible for that divided way you've been feeling. See, he developed the dualism you've been struggling with."

"Dualism?"

"Plato taught that there were two worlds: the world of the ideal and the world of illusion. So dualism is basically the belief that the spiritual world and the real world are two separate worlds, or as us moderns might say, the world of work and the world of the spiritual life are two very different worlds. Other Greek philosophers building on Plato's ideas helped taint our understanding of work. Aristotle, a student of Plato, wrote that there were three different levels in life: the contemplative, the political, and the ordinary. The highest level was the contemplative life. For Aristotle the best life possible was studying philosophy and thinking about the spiritual realities, ethics, etc. If you couldn't devote yourself to spiritual and intellectual contemplation, the next best life was the political life. And if you couldn't be a philosopher or a politician, then you had no choice but to be a worker, a life that the Greeks thought was cursed. The good life was a life which allowed you to escape the drudgery of daily work and devote yourself to spiritual reflection."

"How did Christianity incorporate such thinking?" Brian asked.

"Well, the second century church turned to Plato to help them explain Christian spirituality to the rational-thinking Greeks. One of the ideas that sneaked into our theology during this exchange was dualism – the idea that the spiritual world and the physical world are totally separate."

"Well, in a way isn't Christianity dualistic? I mean, don't we distinguish between the flesh and the spirit?" Brian asked.

"Not at all," Al answered. "The flesh and spirit may be different substances, but they exist in the same world. The Hebrew worldview, the worldview in which Christianity derived, dramatically opposed dualism. Hebrews saw life holistically. For them there was no distinction between the sacred and the secular; in fact, all of life was sacred. The physical world was just as important as the spiritual world. God was present in all of life. All of life was an act of worship."

"Al, are you saying that when Christianity encountered Greek philosophy, and we inherited, or accepted, dualism, we started dividing our world wrongly?"

"Yes. Well, at least we started believing and acting on something that wasn't true. And do you see how this idea moves through time and gets more confusing, more divisive, and more distorted? If you study church history, it doesn't take long to see that the church split into two classes – those who devoted their lives to spiritual things, like monks and priests, and the rest of the world who worked."

Al paused. He could tell Brian was beginning to follow his explanation. "Even great church leaders, men whose words retain much value for the church today, contributed to this thinking. I think it was St. Augustine who said, 'If no one lays a burden on us, we should give ourselves to study and contemplation.' And one of the popes, St. Gregory the Great, said, 'Although the active life is good, the contemplative life is better.' Pretty clear where they were headed with that type of talk."

"Part of me still wants to believe that contemplation is more acceptable to God than making apartment complexes and office buildings. But I also know, and maybe I'm just justifying myself, that apartment buildings provide shelter, and that must please God," Brian said.

"Contemplation is good, we should all have it in the rhythm of our lives," Al agreed, "but it is the more divisive idea, that work is cursed or worldly, that puts us where we have ended up today. When the church started celebrating the life given to prayer, study, and teaching of the scriptures over the life given to work, it could not help but create two spiritual classes of Christians: those believing they were doing higher work, and those believing they were doing lower work."

"I guess in some ways we still believe that?"

"Old ideas die hard. But I think there is a new day dawning. There are new breezes blowing today in the church's teachings on work. But the fact that you have anguished over your offer with such guilt suggests that Plato's ideas may be more alive than you might think."

"So when I begin to dream about making a lot of money in my business so I can sell it and serve God full-time...."

"That's dualism. In your thinking you have to wait to sell before you can serve God. As I said, dualism," Al said.

"And when my friend left his job for the mission field and said he was going into full-time Christian service...."

"More dualism. Jesus would never have used language like that. He said 'follow me' not 'work for me.'"

"And when people compare work to shuffling deck chairs on the Titanic..."

"Dualism."

Al set The Collected Works of Plato on the end table, and looked out the window at the falling snow.

"I was a good priest. I loved it. I still love my church."

"Then why did you leave the church?"

"I didn't leave the church. I left the priesthood."

"Why?"

"By my early forties I was burned out. Our church has a great support system for struggling priests. My congregation gave me a six-month sabbatical. I spent the first two months at a Catholic monastery in Kentucky working with a spiritual director."

"A spiritual director?"

"A spiritual director is someone who helps you listen to what God is saying to you and prepare with you what you are saying to God," Al replied, pouring another cup of coffee. "My spiritual director was a wise man who'd worked with a lot of burned out priests, Episcopal and otherwise. That trip we spent the first two weeks just piecing me back together, helping me recover. I was pretty wiped out."

"And then?"

"Then he asked me a question that changed my life. We were walking through the woods by the monastery. It was November, rainy and wet and gray. All the leaves had fallen and I remember thinking how much the trail resembled my soul, a land heading into winter but with the hope of spring...and he asked me, 'What do you want?'"

"What did you tell him?" Brian asked.

"I don't know exactly. At first I laughed. I stumbled around for words. I think I said something that sounded priestly, like 'I want what everyone wants, to serve God and to serve others well.' Then he laughed gently. 'You don't know what you want, do you?' he said in a fatherly way, and left me to walk alone in the woods."

Brian stirred what was left of the fire.

"I walked for hours that day," Al continued. "Not only had I never asked myself that question before, I don't think I ever even gave myself permission to ask myself that question. To be honest with you, I came home for dinner that night without ever really plunging very deep into that question."

"That must've been pretty scary."

"Yeah, it was. I guess I was afraid of where the question might lead me. And I should've been. The answer would force me to get real."

"So I take it you found your answer?"

"Yes. It took me several weeks of walks and a lot of long talks with my spiritual director. But yes, I found my answer. It's funny how fearful we are of what's in our hearts. Anyway, I finally gave myself permission to ask the question. And, what I truly wanted was to go into business."

"So priests have mid-life crises too! No fast sport cars or young women, but mid-life crises all the same," Brian observed jokingly.

"I wish it were funnier," Al said, making the moment more serious and a little awkward for Brian. "For some priests it is a fast car or a young woman, I assume. Anyway, that period is still a tough time to remember."

"I'm sorry, I didn't mean to make light of it. Please go on."

"It's still a sore spot I guess. A lot of people used your phrase; they said I was having a 'mid-life crisis,' I was 'selling out,' or giving into 'worldliness.' Some close friends, parishioners, people who made their living in the marketplace, seemed to think it was wrong for me to do the same! It was so confusing and strange – they acted like business itself was tainted, stained, and even sinful. It was shocking for them to think of a priest in 'that world,' when they themselves lived in 'that world.' I think I was feeling then what you are feeling now, the awareness of a divided self, the awareness of the dualism still active in so many Christian communities. In my experience then, the message coming from all corners was clear – a life 'in the ministry' is more spiritual than a life in the business world. To leave the ministry for the secular world was something close to losing your faith, especially among my brothers and sisters in the clergy."

"So what did you do?"

"I submitted my resignation and hired on as a junior member of a real estate development company owned by my sister's husband. It wasn't easy. I think even they were a little disconcerted with my decision. But my business education went well, very well. I made a lot of money and helped others make a good bit, too."

"What was the hardest part of the transition?"

"The guilt. For years I felt like I'd betrayed God, like what I was doing was somehow dirty…second-class. It didn't help that some of my former parishioners turned their backs on me…so did some of my fellow priests. It made me want to turn my back on the church. I put my spiritual life on hold around this time and stopped going to church. It just seemed like the two worlds couldn't be reconciled for awhile."

"I thought you said you loved your church?"

"Yes, I do—now. I pursued my spiritual life on my own for many years, and then began to connect with others who were on a similar path. As I learned how to unite my two worlds, I became more comfortable with the role the church can and should play in my life."

The two men sat quietly.

Finally, Brian said, "The gap between my worlds seems to be getting more intense. I'm tired of living a divided life."

"I know how you feel," Al responded, rising from the sofa. Brian rose too.

"Al, maybe one of the reasons we're snowed in this weekend is so we could have this conversation. I'd like to hear more about how you dealt with things. I want to learn what you've learned about bringing the two worlds together."

"Brian, I have enjoyed sharing this time tonight. My calendar is clear. I'm snowed in here like you are," Al responded as he peered out the window at the cascading snowfall. "Why don't we continue the conversation this weekend? Can you meet for breakfast at eight?"

"Sure. Breakfast it is. See you at eight."

# FOUR

.

The sun spilled out of the pale blue Colorado sky and onto the sparkling, bleached-white snow. It created a brilliant, blazing white which poured through big bay windows onto the table where Brian and Al sat, filling the whole restaurant with light.

"So. You left the priesthood and joined your brother-in-law's real estate development firm. You did well. You found your faith resurfaced. What's the rest of the story? How have you managed to be both a devout Christian and a devoted entrepreneur?" Brian asked as he saw Al finishing the last bites of his omelet.

Al took a sip of orange juice and pulled a pen and piece of hotel stationary from his sport-coat pocket. "It's not like I've written a book on this, you know," he smiled. "But I did take some time this morning to jot down a few ideas, a few beliefs, I should say, that have helped me integrate my work life with my spiritual life. They're not very sophisticated; it's not rocket science, as they say. I guess the older I get the more simple life becomes. Anyway, here's my first belief." Al took his pen and wrote across the top of the stationary:

## YOU HAVE DOMINION

"Other religions may have a great deal to say about work, occupational work that is, and spirituality. But I'm a Christian and I go to the Bible for such wisdom," Al began. "I devoted many years to studying those scriptures…it is the only sacred text I know well; so I'm afraid I can't teach you what other faiths believe about this. My thoughts on this subject are shaped by my study of the Bible. You just need to know where I am coming from."

"Fair enough," Brian said.

Al took out a small, leather-bound Bible from his other sport-coat pocket and holding it at arm's length, began flipping through the worn pages. He slid the Bible, opened to the first chapter of Genesis, across the table and said, "I don't have my reading glasses. Read verse 27."

"*God created man in his own image. In the image of god he created him; male and female he created them.*" Brian looked up when he finished the verse.

"Ancient kings put images of themselves in lands where they were establishing their rule," Al explained. "The image of the king was supposed to represent the presence, the rule, the reign of the king." Brian nodded, verifying to Al he was following his thought.

"What's that verse mean to you, Brian?" Al asked.

"It means that both men and women are made in the image of God, for starters. I guess it implies they were made for a purpose."

"That's certainly true. In today's language we'd say, 'God made people in his own image.' But there's more. Keep digging."

Brian thought for a moment. "I suppose it means that being in the image of God, we are God's representatives on earth, like the images of the ancient kings signified a king's rule. That may be our main purpose, to represent God to creation."

"Good," Al replied, pointing to the next verse. "Now read on. The next verse explains how we represent God on earth."

Brian took a sip of coffee, picked up the Bible and read: "Be fruitful and multiply and replenish the earth, and subdue it and have dominion over the fish of the sea, and over the fowl of the air, and over every living thing that moves on the earth."

Brian looked pensively at Al. "Dominion? I'm not sure I follow. That word has always sounded so pushy, or arrogant to me."

"The word just means 'to rule,'" Al offered. "As God's image-bearers, we are to bring God's rule to earth. It's not a 'power trip' because it's God's rule we are bringing, not our own. God is love. He desires to protect, nurture, bless, lead, and support. He wants to see life flourish. And he invites us to help him in this incredible project." Al paused, and then added, "We know from the New Testament that Jesus is the best picture we have of God. Jesus served and cared for others, and he was teaching us about the coming of the kingdom, or as I might say in this context, how to have dominion. So, we should exercise dominion the same way Jesus did – by serving and caring for others."

"I am still a little stuck on what dominion is. What does dominion look like when you see it? What happens when life comes under God's dominion?" Brian asked.

"The Hebrews answered that question with one word: shalom. The word means peace, wholeness, completion, everything returning to its intended design," Al explained.

"So much of life is twisted, distorted, broken. When we bring life back under God's loving rule, we enjoy God's protection, blessing and leadership. Communities can experience shalom. Families can experience shalom. People can experience shalom. When we extend God's dominion we are shalom-making. I like to think of these restorative ministries as the Shalom Project. That's what God is up to on earth – making shalom. And we get to help."

"God's dominion is marked by peace. I'm God's partner. Okay, I understand that. So how am I shalom-making as a construction manager?"

"Flip over to Genesis 2:15 and read what it says."

"The Lord God took the man and put him in the Garden of Eden to work it and take care of it."

"Now," Al said, "answer your own question. How do we establish God's dominion on earth?"

Brian thought, looking intently on the page of Al's worn Bible. "The passage implies that by working in the garden we establish God's dominion, I guess?" Brian offered tentatively, weighing the words even as he spoke them.

"That's what it says. We've seen that we were put on earth to expand the dominion of God, to bring God's protection, leadership and blessing into all of life. Genesis 2:15 explains how we are to do this. Through work."

"We expand God's dominion through work," Brian nodded feeling more satisfied with this revelation. "I think I get it." He took a pen and scrawled on a napkin:

*1. We are made in the image of God.*

*2. God put us here as his representatives to expand his dominion (blessing, protection/nurture).*

*3. The primary way we expand God's dominion is through work.*

"And that is why," Al added enthusiastically, writing across the bottom of the napkin, "you have dominion. The Greeks were wrong, you see," he continued. "Work is not a curse. Work is not a second-class life. Work is how we partner with God in expanding his blessing, protection, and love throughout the earth."

"But what about the scriptures that seem to subject work to less spiritual importance?" Brian replied. "I'm not a Bible scholar like you, but I recall the verse in Matthew about the 'Great Commission.' Jesus says, 'Go and make disciples of all nations.' That's the Great Project isn't it? That's what we are supposed to be about on earth aren't we? Making disciples!"

Al smiled. "You have a point. At the risk of boring you with too much scholarship, let me add a few things."

Brian grinned. "Go ahead. I'm not afraid to learn something new. I'm just accustomed to being a bit cynical; you know; that if something sounds too good, it usually is."

"We studied Greek in seminary, Brian. I know the verse you are talking about. Our English Bibles do have Jesus saying, 'Go and make disciples.' But in the original Greek the verb 'go' is a participle. A better way to translate Jesus' command would be, 'As you are going, make disciples.'"

"'As you are going?' Okay. So 'as we are going,' can mean 'as we are working?'"

"Exactly. Jesus is not saying anything different from what we find in Genesis. We do the work of God while we work. Remember Brian, in the early church people didn't have the luxury of going into 'full-time Christian service.' Everybody worked. Paul worked. He was a tentmaker. Now I'm getting into church history, but it wasn't until the Roman emperor Constantine's conversion in the early fourth century that it was even possible for most people to consider a life of service to God other than working. Brian, I'm convinced the earliest Christians would have seen the workplace as the primary place in which they served God." He paused, "I know it's popular today to think of life as meaningless, as not going anywhere. Work becomes meaningless, too. But when you understand what we've been talking about..." Al pointed to the napkin where he had written the words YOU HAVE DOMINION. "...You realize that every hour you work you are fulfilling your destiny. When you work you are fulfilling the purpose for which you were created, to spread God's loving rule throughout the earth."

Brian thought for a moment. "It's like working in the family business, isn't it?" he said.

"How so?" Al replied.

"The Father owns the business," Brian continued. "He's involved in shalom-making projects all over the earth – he's restoring, reclaiming all that is originally his. And he invites us, his children, to help him."

Brian's mind was buzzing from the coffee and from all the questions popping up in his head. He sat back, happy to be sharing this snowy weekend with Al talking about 'the dominion principle.'

"That's enough theology for one breakfast," Al said mercifully. "Why don't we rent a few snowmobiles and enjoy the sunshine. We can talk more then."

# FIVE

A young man with a skier's tan and a ponytail streaming from beneath a baseball cap wheeled out two Yamaha Warrior snowmobiles from the shed behind the recreation center. Brian and Al were studying a map of winding mountain trails that they had picked up at the lobby shortly after breakfast.

"The map won't be too helpful today," the young man said. "The trails are covered with fresh powdered snow. Don't go too far; stay on this side of the ridge and you'll be fine. And watch the sky. They say more snow is on the way."

Within minutes Brian and Al were roaring up a trail that cut through thick, snow-laden evergreens and across a frozen river until it opened up into a glade surrounded by towering mountain birches. The two riders cut their engines. A deafening mountain silence thanked them in reply.

"Have you ever been married, Al?"

"Yes. My wife Martha and I married shortly after I left the priesthood. I lost her to cancer in '95. You mentioned last night that you were divorced. What caused the break up, Brian?"

"Ironically, a lot of it had to do with my work. She said I worked too much, that work was my mistress."

"Was it?" Al asked.

"I suppose. Yes it was." Brian thought for a moment. "Work gave me what I needed – security, significance. I guess I didn't think I really needed God."

"And then?"

"Eventually I figured out that life was drudgery without God – even when work was going well. My friends said I was just beginning to pay attention to the spiritual side of life. Whatever you want to call it, I began a relationship with God." The two men paused to watch an eagle glide effortlessly across the sky.

"Did your spiritual awakening have any impact on your work?" Al asked.

"It created a lot of tension I didn't feel before!" Brian laughed.

Al thought for a moment. "Have you ever heard the story about the two brick-layers?"

"No, but I suspect I am about to," Brian teased.

"A woman was walking down a sidewalk in a European city when she encountered a haggard-looking man laying bricks. He was obviously unhappy. He grumbled as he pushed his wheelbarrow and haphazardly threw the bricks into place. He took no pride in his work.

'What are you doing?' the visitor asked.

'What does it look like I'm doing, lady?' the bricklayer said with disgust. 'I'm laying brick.'

A few yards further down the sidewalk the woman met another bricklayer. This man, however, seemed to love his job. He whistled as he pushed his wheelbarrow and carefully placed each brick into place. He took great pride in his work.

'What are you doing?' the woman asked the second bricklayer.

'I'm building a great cathedral,' he beamed proudly.

Both men were working at the same job. The first brick-layer hated his work because he had no vision for the glorious cathedral he was helping to create. The second bricklayer loved his work because he could see the bigger vision. He was honored to participate in such a great project."

"The cathedral we are building is a better world," Brian recognized.

"Right," Al concurred. "When we see that our work is part of God's glorious project to heal the world, work takes on much greater significance."

"I love the construction business, but I'm not sure I'd say I'm healing the world through it. I'm not sure I am...what did you call it?...shalom-making when I rehab apartments."

"Let's think that through, Brian. Pick one of the jobs you feel proudest of."

"The Nickel Creek project in Birmingham. We rehabbed 135 units in six months, under budget, and had a healthy net profit. The property manager was so impressed she set up a lunch with her parent company and they've con-tracted with us to do five more of their complexes next year in cities across the southeast."

"What else makes you proud of that project?" Al probed.

"It was a win for everybody. Whoever had been manag-ing the property had pretty much just let it go. There was a lot of turnover. The tenants didn't feel safe. They didn't know their neighbors, or want to. Gang graffiti covered some of the walls. There had even been a drug bust. Today Nickel Creek is a hot property again. We put in new kitchens, new roofs, painted everything on site, and paved the parking lot. We also threw in a few extras our contract didn't call for."

"Extras?"

"We built a playground. We put in a walking trail."

"How do the tenants feel now?" Al asked.

"They love it. A lot of construction people won't touch rehab work. It's hard because you have to work around people who are living there and you can't start from scratch. But we are becoming very good at it. We train our people to respect the tenants they are working with. And most of the time they do. We threw a big party for the whole complex when the job was done. People stayed long after dark. The property manager works for us now. We've given her a larger vision for what she is responsible for. She's hired an activities coordinator who is creating opportunities for folks to get to know one another. Nickel Creek now has English lessons for their Hispanic tenants. They offer painting classes. Starting next week the residents are starting a 'Nickel Creek Community Task Force' that will get together every month to talk about life in their complex and how they can make it better."

"What was your relationship like with the subs?"

"The subs like working with us, too. That is, the ones that we didn't have to fire," Brian laughed. "Our standards are pretty high. The subs we finally settled in with do good work and like to work for us. We help them build their business while we build ours. They've even become more efficient as the workload has gone through the roof. Those relationships will serve all of us well in the years to come."

"How many people worked for you directly on the project?"

"We had five of our people on-site all the time. We worked like dogs because we knew we only had six months. It reminded me of playing football in high school and going through two-a-days in August. You become close after working so hard. Our team got really tight. Sometimes, though, I felt more like a pastor than a construction manager. This was one young guy's first job out of college. He was lost when he came to us. He used to whine all the time about how hard it was going to be not having two weeks off at Christmas and a week for spring break! He grew up a lot at Nickel Creek. We talked about everything – the big questions – and we taught him to work hard, deal with difficult people, and not to cut corners. He started that job as a boy. He left it a man."

"Sounds like shalom has come to Nickel Creek," Al said, enjoying Brian's enthusiasm. "God gave you dominion over the Nickel Creek job. You were given responsibility and you used it to serve the tenants, the subs, your team, and the apartment owners. You used your dominion to bless, nurture, serve and protect. That's what it means to extend God's dominion through work."

An eagle circled overhead. Brian noticed a bank of gray clouds pushing in from the north. The wind felt colder as the edge of the cloud bank eclipsed the sun.

Al pointed overhead. "Do you see how that eagle rides the wind so effortlessly?" Brian nodded in response as the two watched the bird arc across the sky. "When we are working in our area of dominion, work is like that eagle's flight. Even though it is hard work, it appears effortless because it's riding the wind. Jesus said these words at the end of his life, 'I have brought you glory on earth by completing the work you gave me to do,'" Al recited. "We all have work God has given us to do. When we are working in the place God designed for us, we work with the wind and the flying comes a whole lot easier."

Brian remembered a movie he had seen when he was a boy. Chariots of Fire told the story of Eric Liddell, a Scottish Olympian who refused fame and glory as a runner in order to keep his Sabbath for God. Liddell once said, "When I run I feel His pleasure." Brian knew that feeling, too. He often felt God's pleasure when he finished a job on time and under budget, or worked through a messy personnel issue in a way that left both parties with a win.

"One of the reasons I burned out as a priest, I think, is because I wasn't soaring with the wind. I was flapping against it," Al continued. "God had made me for something else, and I was fighting it. When I finally found my new assignment, I felt a freedom I hadn't known in a long, long time."

"I really think I'm soaring on the wind," Brian said. "...Even if sometimes I have to fight to stay there. Construction is a very competitive business. And my company is pretty competitive internally as well."

"The business world plays hardball," Al agreed. "It's no place for weak people. It's not easy to establish God's dominion on earth. The world we live in is broken, twisted, and fallen. There are dark powers at work that resist what God wants to do. I buckle my helmet on each morning and get ready to take a few hits before lunch. That's just the way business is these days."

Brian resonated strongly with Al's metaphor of work as a kind of warfare. "When the competitor in me comes out – when I really fight to get a deal or work the angles so that a promotion goes my way – that's when I feel the biggest gulf between my spiritual life and my work life," Brian admitted. "Christians always talk about being the same person on Sunday as you are on Monday, but I'm sorry. The world I live in on Mondays is a much meaner world than the world I live in on Sundays. I'm not proud of how hard I have to hit sometimes to make the tackle. But that's the way it has to be."

"I don't think being a spiritual person means you can't play for keeps," Al replied. "I think what we are talking about here goes deeper. You know the story of Abraham and Lot, right?"

"The Old Testament is hard for me to follow. Refresh my memory," Brian said.

"Okay, but first follow me. Get on your machine."

Brian, slightly confused, got back on his snowmobile. The two machines roared to life and Al took off back down the trail they had ridden in on. Halfway down the mountain, Al turned off the main trail onto a narrower path that went sharply uphill. Brian followed. Ten minutes later the trail opened to an overlook with a spectacular view of a vast, snow-covered valley. Brian followed Al's lead and cut the motor. Both men were awed by the splendor of the view. To the left the resort lay tucked away in gentle hills, a stubborn snow-plow working the road leading to the resort. Smoke from the chimneys of another upscale resort a mile up the road disappeared into the gray sky. However, the eastern vista reminded Brian of a moonscape, with great boulders scattered along the rugged mountainside. Brian noticed a landslide had ripped through a section of the mountain crushing everything in its wake – broken trees poked out of the snow like broken bones sticking out of flesh.

"I'm in the real estate business," Al softly broke the silence. "Suppose I am in a very generous mood and I wanted to give you some real estate to develop. In fact, I'm going to give you half the valley to develop. One of us will take the western valley. One of us will take the eastern valley. Which half of the valley would you choose to develop, Brian?" "The western half, obviously," Brian replied. "The land to the east is almost worthless. You couldn't do anything with it."

"Abraham and his nephew Lot were in a similar situation," Al explained as they looked over the valley. "Abraham and Lot's families grew and they decided they needed to go separate ways. Abraham gave Lot first choice of whatever land he wanted. Lot, like any good real estate developer, took the choicest land. Abraham settled for the less desirable piece. Later in Genesis we discover that Lot got into trouble and Abraham prospered."

"Letting someone choose prime real estate right out from under you is no way to run a business," Brian muttered.

"I don't think these stories tell us how to run our businesses," Al replied. "I do think they show us something about what our hearts need to be like if we are to have dominion. Abraham was confident that if he lived the right way and did the right things God would take care of him. Lesser men would have started a war with Lot, or tried to manipulate him politically. Abraham didn't fight with Lot."

"I know this is the tough part about being a Christian in the business world, but you have to fight to get ahead," Brian countered. "The business world is built on competition."

"And competition is good," Al said. "We all benefit from it. But there is a fine ethical line between competing fairly and manipulative striving." Al returned to his snowmobile and pulled a Power Bar from his backpack. "I began working with a software company in the eighties that was about to go public. Two engineers started it. Sales took off and they began staffing up. Two of their earliest hires were hi-tech whiz kids straight out of college, Monica and Pete. Monica loved her work. She knew she was brilliant and I'm certain she anticipated growing with the company. She didn't constantly crow about it though. She just kept turning out great work day after day, year after year, and in time she emerged as a star in the company. Today she is a VP and on the senior management team. I was told the CEO is grooming her to take his spot. Pete, on the other hand, was always obsessed with 'making it big.' He knew he was sharp, and wanted everyone else to know it, too. He griped about everything: the size of his office, his bonus, his title, what hotels he stayed in on the road. He got on everybody's nerves. He played dirty, too. He didn't really like Monica and would speak disparagingly about her to other managers. Pete was a piece of work. He took credit for accomplishments that weren't really his. Pete wasn't satisfied with proving himself, either. He always wanted to be a rung higher up the ladder than where he was. He never felt he was being appreciated for his 'great' talents. Last time I dropped in for a visit Pete wasn't there. I was told they let him go a couple of years ago. Mutual friends tell me he's still looking for work – they say that he thinks most entry level jobs are beneath his level of expertise."

Brian grabbed an apple from his coat pocket and took a bite. "I think I see what you are saying, Al. When we find the place where God assigns us – our dominion – we need to be content with it and work it with excellence. But what about being successful, being driven? Is it wrong to want to expand your dominion? Honestly, if I stay in business I am going to want to move up in my company. I always enjoy more responsibility and I'm not necessarily against making more money. Is that all wrong?"

"I had a similar conversation once with a friend of mine who is a CEO of a large gas company. He put it like this: 'If you work hard and do the right thing, God will take care of the promotions.' We focus on working hard and smart. We let God worry about the rest."

All of a sudden Brian became aware of the amount of activity taking place on the overlook, something he realized Al was already studying. Snow clouds the color of gunmetal had moved in over the ridge. The wind pushed snow in silent clumps from heavy branches of bent treetops. The eagle had finally stopped circling and settled into its nest. A family of rabbits scurried lightly atop the snow heading for their burrow. A doe and two fawns appeared briefly, and then disappeared into a thicket.

"Brian, what are the animals doing now?"

"Getting ready for a change in the weather, like we ought to be doing."

Al laughed, "You are right. Let's head down the mountain. But first take a good look at this scene and remember what you are seeing. We could learn something here."

# SIX

Steam rose from the outdoor hot tub, perched on a deck. A nicely shoveled path stopped short of the stairs that led to a pool, now covered for the winter and buried in more than a foot of snow. Brian and Al darted through snowflakes and jumped into the hot water, sending more steam into the snowy sky.

"Now, about those animals. What am I supposed to learn from them other than they know when to get out of the cold?"

"That's the lesson," Al replied matter-of-factly. "The weather changes. Seasons change. Life is always changing. Animals have an intuitive sense of when the change is coming and how they should respond. We humans are not always so smart."

"I am not quite sure what that has to do with dominion?"

"Dominion changes, too. Our assignments change. Our role changes. Our place changes. Do you know that the average American worker will change careers, not jobs but careers, six times in his lifetime?"

"Our company is always changing," Brian related over the noise of bubbling water. "The organizational chart is always shifting, people are joining the team or moving on; most people don't stay forever. Privately, I've always resented this. I thought it was a sign that we were not very mature as a company. I have to admit, I don't like change."

"All living things change, Brian. That's how you can tell they are alive. Life is fluid, dynamic, and organic. Life ebbs and flows. There are seasons in business life just as there are seasons in the woods."

Brian laughed. "I just had a picture of those animals we saw up on the outlook. What if the doe was like me and said, 'This stinks. I'm staying where I am. I don't care if I freeze; at least I know where everything is.' Or what if the rabbit had decided to file a lawsuit because she didn't like the new weather pattern?"

"The irony is that we do that all the time," Al said. "Rather than respond to the change and welcome it as one of the rhythms of life, we fight it. And sometimes we die as a result. There's a poem in the Book of Ecclesiastes that says it best:

> *There is a time for everything and a season*
> *for every activity under heaven:*
> *A time to be born and a time to die,*
> *A time to plant and a time to uproot,*
> *A time to kill and a time to heal,*
> *A time to tear down and a time to build,*
> *A time to weep and a time to laugh,*
> *A time to mourn and a time to dance,*
> *A time to scatter stones and a time to gather*
> *them,*
> *A time to embrace and a time to refrain,*

> *A time to search and a time to give up,*
> *A time to keep and a time to throw away,*
> *A time to tear and a time to mend,*
> *A time to be silent and a time to speak,*
> *A time to love and a time to hate,*
> *A time for war and a time for peace.'*

"Our culture celebrates times of birth and new beginnings," Al continued. "We don't understand that seasons of death are part of life too. Without death there is no new life."

"Last year we sold off part of a subsidiary company we had owned for quite awhile. Most of us saw that as a defeat. By your definition our company was preserving its health!" Brian said, pondering Al's words. "My company changes a lot. Our CEO doesn't mind birthing and he doesn't mind burying either! I have to say I have never really liked it. One of the confusing things with all the changes we have experienced is discovering where the new lines are drawn, I mean with departments, job descriptions. Change is tough that way. We have had difficulties distinguishing boundaries after some of those changes. We've gotten into some pretty nasty 'turf wars' over the years."

"Turf wars?"

"I have seen fights over clients. Our sales department will butt heads with accounting. There have been major communication issues because departments don't necessarily trust each other. I admit I resent it when someone from another department pushes his nose into our business. Oh, and when resources are scarce, I have seen ugly fights between peers for a piece of the pie."

"Brian, hold that thought. See if you can apply the dominion principle to your company's turf wars. What would your company look like if everyone understood dominion?"

Brian thought for a moment. "I guess we'd respect the dominion of others. We'd have a clear understanding of our roles. We'd know where the property lines were and we'd respect them."

"Very good. I like your image of 'property lines.' Property has been an important idea in our tradition. Not to bore you with my historical musing again, but ancient Greeks and Romans saw property as sacred. Children were trained to identify and respect property markers. I remember when I was little my mother told me not to cross through the Severson's backyard; she told me to respect their private property. How about the bible; can you think of any biblical examples of respecting dominion?"

There was a brief silence as Brian searched for a good example. "How about King David?" he finally offered. "Everyone thought he should replace Saul as king. He even had an opportunity to kill Saul and take the throne. But he didn't."

Al added, "David said, 'I will not lift my hand against my master, because he is the Lord's anointed.' That is a great example. David respected the dominion of Saul. He knew dominion, the crown, the anointing, was God's to give and God's to take away."

Brian was silent for a long time.

"What are you thinking?" Al asked.

"I'm pretty driven at work. I'm a 'take no prisoners' type of manager. I'm thinking maybe I'm one of the reasons for some of the chaos at the office. I'm so competitive, so driven to expand my piece of the pie, that when I see a guy struggling, I move in and start taking over a little bit at a time. I've gotten pretty good at moving the property lines to my advantage."

"Sometimes, we discover the enemy, and it is us. How might you approach this differently now that you understand the dominion principle?"

"My first question ought to be: who has dominion over this? If I do not, then my goal should be to strengthen the person who does. I ought to honor and protect the dominion of others, not steal it."

"Any other applications?"

"I can see how we'd cooperate better. The threat level is gone." Brian paused. "I know there was a time when my business was my god. Turf wars are inevitable when you think that way. If your turf is your god then you have to guard it, expand it – even by stealing turf – because your life depends on it, because it is your life." Al nodded. "But," Brian continued, "If my work is a gift to me, a dominion assignment, then I am not threatened by the size or success of another's dominion."

Brian let his own words sink in. "But there is still something I don't understand. God does call us to expand our dominion, doesn't he? Isn't there a story Jesus tells about being faithful in little and then being entrusted with much? Isn't there a parable of a tiny mustard seed growing into a big tree? When is it right to expand dominion? When is it wrong?"

Al held up a pruny-looking hand. "Why don't we continue the discussion later? I'm shriveling up. If I stay in here any longer I am going to be one big wrinkle. Why don't we pick it up again at dinner?"

# SEVEN

Brian could've continued the discussion, but honored Al's desire for a break. These conversations were really stimulating. He had a few points he wanted to make during the last exchange, and was afraid he might forget them before tonight. At the risk of pestering Al, Brian decided to shoot him an e-mail with a few ideas. He had several hours before dinner that he would use to process his conversations with Al and pre-think tonight's discussion. He didn't want to wear Al out, but one e-mail wouldn't hurt. It might make tonight more profitable.

He opened the laptop and let it purr to life. From the desktop he clicked his e-mail icon and started his draft:

*From: brian_tucker@vanguardconstruction.com*
*To: alhunt@venturecap.com*
*Re: Thoughts for our next discussion. (Who knows, the snow might stop and we might actually have to leave this place on Monday!)*
*Al — Enjoyed our time so far. Am looking forward to tonight. Thought I'd take a shot at summarizing what I've learned so far, then ask a few questions.*

*WHAT I HAVE LEARNED SO FAR*
*1. We are made in the image of God.*
*2. God put us here as His representatives to expand his dominion.*
*3. The primary way we expand God's dominion is through work.*

*DEFINING DOMINION*
*Dominion. God's gentle rule. God is restoring all of life to its original purpose and design. He gives His dominion to His children so we can bring God's blessing, protection, and leadership into all of life. We're all in the family business.*
*QUESTIONS*
*FIRST QUESTION. They say the number one mistake young companies make is expanding too quickly. I've seen lots of our competitors get greedy and go into markets they weren't prepared for and pay the consequences. Could you take me through the finer points of how the dominion principle applies here?*
*SECOND QUESTION. The last company I worked for had the opposite problem. We never took risks, never went after opportunities. I see a lot of people like that around my current office. They seem to think that the goal of the game is to let the clock run out...they play defense all the time. Could you take me through the finer points of how the dominion principle applies for risk-adverse companies?*
*THIRD QUESTION. A friend of mine built his company, and then sold it. He probably doesn't ever have to work again. Yet now he regrets the*

*decision. He says he gave up more than he thought he was giving up when he let his business go. Did he give away his dominion?*

*FOURTH QUESTION. Why do so many good people change, get corrupted when they get what they ask for – i.e., greater dominion? Success ruins so many people. What pitfall am I not seeing when it comes to success and dominion?*

*I'm not sure you will even open this until tonight, but at least I had a chance to put my thoughts down. See you soon.*

*Brian Tucker*
*Senior Construction Manager*
*Vanguard Corporation*

# EIGHT

It seemed the hostess had hardly seated them before Al and Brian were combing through the questions Brian had left for Al earlier. Al, like Brian, checked his e-mail every afternoon. He hated to miss an opportunity to respond to work.

"You asked about the dangers of taking dominion when God has not asked you to," Al said, stirring Equal® into his iced tea. A waiter brought two Caesar salads and a loaf of sour dough bread. Brian cut a piece and buttered it. "This happens all the time," Al went on. "And when the right person takes the wrong job, the result is deadly. I call this the Uzzah principle."

"What's the Uzzah principle?" Brian asked.

"Uzzah carried the ark of the covenant for King David back into Jerusalem. The ark fell, Uzzah touched it, and God struck him dead."

"I'm sorry, Al, stories like that bother me."

"They bother me, too," Al admitted. "That story bothered me so much I once spent an entire day trying to figure it out."

"And?" Brian asked skeptically.

"First I found that Uzzah was probably a good guy trying to do the right thing. David was trying to reform Israel so he wanted to bring the ark back to its home in Jerusalem. The biblical account, which you'll find in the second book of Samuel, even says that people where rejoicing as the ark made its way back to Jerusalem."

"Then why was Uzzah killed?" Brian asked.

"You'll find the story retold in the book of Chronicles" Al responded. "There the author reminds us that only Levites were supposed to carry the ark. God had given the tribe of Levi dominion over the ark. Uzzah wasn't a Levite. He was the right guy doing the wrong job – a job he didn't have dominion over. And he lost his life for it."

"I get the point, but that still seems pretty harsh," Brian allowed.

"Again, we don't look at these stories as Harvard case studies for running a business. We look to scriptures for ancient wisdom. Uzzah took dominion that wasn't his, and he died. This is a very representative example of what happens when we appropriate dominion today."

"Do you have a more current example?" Brian wanted to know.

"Sure. This one comes from American history. Meriwether Lewis ranks as one of the greatest explorers in history. Thomas Jefferson sent him and his life-long friend, William Clark, on an 8,000-mile journey to explore the American west; they were sent to find a water passage linking the Atlantic with the Pacific. They never found the fabled passage, but they did return three-and-a half years later as national heroes, having successfully battled grizzlies, starvation, sickness, and Indians.

Lewis became the darling of Washington, cruising from one party to the next, celebrated for his extraordinary accomplishment. President Jefferson appointed Lewis governor of the Louisiana Territory shortly after his return. History shows that this was a tragic mistake. The unique gifts and skills that made Lewis a brilliant explorer worked against him in his new role as a politician and businessman. He became depressed; he starting drinking too much and incurred great debt. Finally, mired in despair, he killed himself in an inn outside Nashville, Tennessee. I've seen his grave. It's marked by a broken shaft and a plaque that remembers 'the violent and untimely end of a bright and glorious career.'"

"And the moral of that story is that not every promotion is a good promotion," Brian said.

"True. Dominion assignments are seasonal, but we need to make sure God is the one changing our assignment before we move on. Do you remember that eagle we saw this morning? We want to stay with the wind. Sometimes we take new assignments because they are challenging and attractive. But they were not meant for us to take. I see the eagle, flapping hard to stay aloft, growing tired and faltering."

The waiter brought steaks and refilled their glasses. Buttering his potato, Al said, "Your second question — about companies and people who always play defense and never take risks — brings into focus the other side of the principle we were just discussing. There are times when it is wrong to take dominion. There are other times when it is wrong not to take it. Jesus told a story once that illustrates this. A wealthy man gave three managers who worked for him different sums of money and told them to invest it. The first two made wise investments and he praised them. The third manager didn't invest his money at all because he was afraid to take the risk. The wealthy man praised the two managers who risked and invested and scolded the manager who did not."

Brian finished cutting his steak and said, "Evidently, Jesus wants us to take risks, to stretch, to expand dominion."

"That's why I invest in new companies," Al said. "It can

be a great way to expand dominion. It's a risk. But I'm convinced that one of the greatest ways to bless any community is to start new businesses in it."

"But how do you know when it's time to expand and when it's time to sit tight?"

"Now that's the million dollar question!"

"You face that question every day, Al, in your venture capital business. You choose to invest in some companies and not in others. How do you know?"

"There's not a magical formula, I'm afraid. I do my homework. Does this opportunity make sense? Is it a good fit for me? I get wise counsel from my board. I run the numbers. I put the business through an ethical filter – am I going to be happy with the product they produce? And then I do my internal work."

"What's that?"

"Business for spiritually-minded people is more than running the numbers and having a great board. Business also involves listening to God. Prayer. Reflection. I pray about my business decisions. I discuss them with my spiritual director. I wait for a sense of inner peace before I say yes."

"Really? Does your spiritual director know a lot about your line of work?" Brian asked, somewhat astonished.

"No. I don't talk to him about venture capital, Brian," Al replied, realizing Brian had missed the point. "I talk to him to find out what God is saying to me. His role in my life is to help me listen to God, not to tell me what I should do. I always spend some time with him before any major decision. He helps me slow down and listen to God."

"Wow. That didn't even occur to me. I do pray for work, but in a very general way. It makes sense though, to pray with your spiritual director, someone invested at the 'ground floor' of your spiritual life," Brian said.

"Now let me have a go at this steak and you talk a bit. Tell me more about the friend you mentioned in your e-mail, the gentlemen who sold his business but is now second-guessing. I've seen it before. I've seen a few friends ascend to the heights of the 'American dream' only to find despair," Al said with a wry smile.

"My friend Gene owned a small chain of restaurants in the southeast – Atlanta, Charlotte, Knoxville, Nashville. Great operation; he had great service, the food was a bit pricey but incredible, he was pulling in business hand over fist. On a Saturday night you could easily expect to wait 45 minutes to an hour to be seated. Anyway, as happens so often, his successful little operation was noticed by a national chain, they made him an offer he couldn't refuse. Today he's set for life and couldn't be more miserable."

"I have to tell you I am not totally surprised."

"I am. When he managed the business I heard him complain all the time about the long hours, the amount of travel, and the stress of keeping a good kitchen. For years he dreamed of selling out. Now he's so unhappy. He says he never understood what he had until he gave it away. All of a sudden he's saying, 'Oh, Brian, you don't understand. It's an amazing privilege to own a business. It's a wonderful responsibility. The closest thing I can compare it to is having children. When you own a business you are supporting so many people's hopes and dreams; the cooks, the waitresses, the hostesses, the managers. You provide a living for them and healthcare and car payments. You become part of the community. And if that isn't enough, this business, this aggravating, stressful, frustratingly wonderful thing provides for you and your family.' I don't think I'm exaggerating when I say he's grieving the loss of his business like the death of a loved one."

"Giving up something like that can be very traumatic," Al observed.

"He also told me that he never felt more spiritually alive than when he was running his company. Before he sold out, he always said that retiring early would help him get closer to God with the extra time and the financial flexibility. But now he says that the holiest place he'd ever been was at the helm of his business. That was where he cared for people, spoke into their lives, wept with them, prayed with them, and helped them figure out where life was going. He was very 'hands-on.'"

"It sounds like he gave away his dominion without thinking it through," Al said quietly. "Have you heard of the story of Jacob and Esau? Esau sold his birthright, which was the right to lead his family, to Jacob for a bowl of soup. He also forfeited his dominion without weighing the consequences."

"I guess my friend doesn't have much of a success story, after all; unless you believe work, building something, is cursed, and the idle life of absolute leisure is blessed. If you look at the situation through the filter of dualism, then I guess he hit the jackpot. Sometimes Gene used to bellyache so much it was like he was imprisoned, trapped by that little restaurant chain. But if work is truly the way we expand God's dominion on earth, he sold his platform pretty cheaply. I guess I'd be miserable, too."

"Very well put," Al agreed, spearing one last bite of steak before the waiter cleared the table. Recognizing that Brian wasn't finished processing it all, Al went ahead and ordered some coffee, so Brian wouldn't feel rushed.

"Have you read The Prayer of Jabez by Bruce Wilkinson?" Brian asked. "It's about asking God to expand your borders. It really pertains to the same thing we are talking about, expanding dominion."

"I would agree. It's nice to see a book like that make the New York Times' best seller list."

"Evidently, there are a lot people responding to that innate desire to expand dominion. We did The Prayer of Jabez in my growth group, me and a few other guys. I liked the book a lot, but after talking to you, I don't know if I got the right message entirely," Brian said. "And I have heard other people voice concerns with the book."

"What concerns?" Al asked.

"Well, considering the popularity of the book, I would assume there are many people seeking to expand their dominion, and I'm just not sure we are all ready. I speak for myself, too, I guess," Brian replied. "I remember being a young go-getter, wanting it all, wanting all the challenges and responsibilities life could bring, and if I would've gotten a tenth of what I wanted, I would've crashed big time. Too much responsibility too soon can be a killer. I've seen careers sink like a rock when people have gotten in over their heads."

"I once heard a weightlifter say that the most important skill a weightlifter can have during training is knowing when to add more weight to his lift," Al volunteered. As he reached in his pocket for a pen he continued, "And that leads us to perhaps the most important dominion principle." He wrote purposefully on a clean napkin:

### THE HEART MUST BE PREPARED FOR DOMINION

"Expanded dominion requires an expanded heart. Serious spiritual preparation must occur before we are ready to pray the prayer of Jabez," Al went on, his voice stern and serious. "In fact, I'm much more comfortable asking God to help me be faithful within my present dominion. I am confident He will expand my dominion when He is ready, so anymore, I seldom even ask."

"Sounds like there is a story behind that one."

"There is. But I'm not sure I want to tell it."

# NINE

"Well, I would be honored to hear your story, if you would be gracious enough to tell it," Brian offered.

The waiter came to top off the coffee cups. From the way Al was acting, a bit sheepish, uncomfortable, Brian could tell that whatever story was behind this lesson, it was a painful one. Al's eyes grew cloudy; he looked a little embarrassed.

"Underneath it all, I am a very private person, and if I have been exceedingly private with you this evening, it is because there are some things I am not proud of, some lessons that reveal the worst things in me. I have enjoyed counseling you this weekend; it has been a pleasure sharing whatever wisdom I suppose I have. But you have been very open and honest with me, and I owe you that much," Al said softly. "You may find this funny, or pathetic, but I know once I tell you this you may not look up to me so much, and forgive me, but I have enjoyed being looked up to. You'd think a sixty-two year old man wouldn't be so vain, so foolish, but truth be told, I am."

"You have been genuine with me. I appreciate it, and I'm old enough to recognize that 'heroes' are human, too,"

Brian encouraged. "If we have built trust over the last couple of days, then rest assured that the trust could only deepen."

"You are quite a young man, Brian, and you'd honor me if you would hear this story. I've made plenty of mistakes in my life, but none of them come close to the pain I feel when I remember this one." Al sipped his coffee and leaned slightly back into his chair. Speaking clearly, but quietly, he continued. "In the late eighties I went into the real estate business. I don't know if you can remember, but the market was really hot, and I made a ton of money very quickly. I hadn't been out of the priesthood very long and I'd never had money before. Getting some was intoxicating, but I guess that is just an excuse. Well, I decided to leave the firm I was with and go out on my own. I didn't realize it then but what a mistake that was! On my own I wanted to succeed, but without accountability, without guidance, without help from anyone. For once I wanted to be a self-made man." A dour grin appeared on Al's face and then vanished. "Anyway," he continued, "life grew pretty dark in the midst of all that."

"Did you fail? Did you go broke?" Brian asked.

"No. Just the opposite; I made quite a bit more money going solo. But it came at a cost. I lost my way spiritually, could've lost my wife, and for a while I completely lost myself. During that time I became a very unpleasant person to be around, puffed up, critical, impatient. I want to say that it was because after so many years of denying myself and caring for others, I wanted to indulge myself, but that would be a cop-out. What I was getting into was abject selfishness, and I knew it. I was playing with was death. After a time, my secretary became my lover. When I wanted out, she didn't. It got ugly, with jealous threats and a lot of hurting one another. All the time I was so phony around my wife, waiting for the other shoe to drop. My wife never knew, as far as I know. Maybe she did, maybe she just saved me the shame of facing it." Al stared at his coffee mug for a moment; his eyes were very weak and watery. "I had a lot of power, in those days. Money, some prestige, but it darkened my soul, muffled my conscience. I grew blind to what was important to me. I lost my center."

"How did you find your way back?"

"You are going to laugh, but it was my spiritual director."

"I'm not laughing. I respect you for confiding in him. If I've learned one thing this weekend, I've learned I need one of those. I need to find myself a good spiritual director." Brian's voice was earnest, "Please continue."

"Several years into what I call my selfish years, I took a spiritual retreat at the same monastery I had stayed in when I decided to leave the priesthood. My director was in his eighties by then, but still agreed to see me. We hadn't spent any time together in years. 'My walk,' as you say, in those days was little more than a crawl, but I knew enough to know I was in trouble. My director heard me graciously. He didn't say a whole lot, I think he was grieved to see where I had sunk, but he gave me a copy of Henri Nouwen's book, In the Name of Jesus. That book helped pull me out of the pit I was in. It's one of the most important books I've ever read. In fact, I keep it with me."

Al reached into his briefcase and pulled out a thin paperback with yellowed, dog-eared pages. "Nouwen was a priest and writer who taught at Harvard and Yale. He was at the so-called 'top' of his career when he burned out. He shocked everyone by becoming a chaplain at a home for the mentally handicapped. That's where he wrote this," Al said as he picked up the book and began leafing through it. "It's about the spiritual lessons he had to learn to retool his heart for leadership."

"How does Nouwen describe the journey?"

"He describes the lessons as movements. These movements are what must happen in our hearts for us to be prepared for expanded dominion. He describes three movements of the heart. I've memorized them I've read this so often." Al spoke them as he wrote them on a fresh napkin:

*"From relevance to prayer.*

*From popularity to ministry.*

*From leading to being led."*

"First, Nouwen says, we must move from relevance to prayer. The desire to be successful or relevant must give way to a sense of being anchored in the love of God. Listen to this...," Al pulled a pair of reading glasses out of his coat pocket and thumbed to what appeared to be a familiar page.

> *"It is not enough for the (leaders) of the future to be moral people, well-trained, eager to help their fellow humans, and able to respond creatively to the burning issues of their time. All of that is valuable and important, but it is not the heart of Christian leadership. The central question is: Are the leaders of the future truly men and women of God, people with an ardent desire to dwell in God's presence, to listen to God's voice, to look at God's beauty, to touch God's incarnate Word, and to taste fully God's infinite goodness?"*

"We must also move from popularity to ministry," Al continued. "Nouwen warns us to be wary of the need to be spectacular, to be a hero, and says those desires must be replaced by a simple desire to serve people." Al flipped several more pages and continued to read:

> *"The leadership about which Jesus speaks is of a radically different kind from the leadership*

*offered by the world. It is a servant-leadership...in which the leader is a vulnerable servant who needs the people as much as they need him or her.*

*From this it is clear that a whole new type of leadership is asked for...a leadership which is not modeled on the power games of the world, but on the servant-leader, Jesus.'*

"Finally, Nouwen describes the transition from leading to being led. The temptation is always to abuse the power associated with dominion; to use this power to serve ourselves, our egos." Al took his glasses off and put them back in his pocket. "Read the paragraph I have my finger on. I think it is important to our discussion tonight." Al handed the open book to Brian. The page was almost completely highlighted, the margins around it filled with barely legible notes written in fading blue ink. Brian read the paragraph aloud.

*"It is not a leadership of power and control, but a leadership of power and humility ... Powerlessness and humility in the spiritual life do not refer to people who have no spine and who let everyone else make decisions for them. They refer to people who are so deeply in love with Jesus that they are ready to follow him wherever he guides them, always trusting that, with him, they will find life and find it abundantly."*

"You were right to be concerned about expanding dominion, Brian. Most people don't give it enough thought, and sadly, usually they should've, because more often than not, they can't handle the increase. More people have been destroyed by taking on expanded dominion before cultivating a bigger heart, than those who have languished away, waiting for God to deliver an assignment befitting the size of their heart." The eloquence nearly caught Brian off guard. Al stopped, sipped his coffee and leaned into the table squarely in front of Brian. "By the way," he said, "how old are you?"

"I was thirty-five in August."

"You are at a very important age. You are heading into what I call 'deep adulthood.' It is the age when most people suffer truth because pretending just doesn't cut it anymore. It's a fruitful time spiritually, if you are willing to lean into your faith, if you are willing to listen to God. God uses deep adulthood; He knows how to capitalize on this period of transition, or maturity. Often, I think He uses deep adulthood to prepare us for our next assignment, for our expanded dominion."

"Then why do so many mid-life transitions come off as mid-life crises?" Brian asked.

"Because most people don't take the time to learn the lessons," Al responded. "We are talking about deep soul work here. Most people focus on their circumstances, on the paycheck. They don't take the time to ask the hard questions that really prepare them for expanded dominion."

"Not everyone has access to a monk versed in market economics and family counseling?" Brian teased.

"You don't need a monk," Al replied with a playful sigh. "All you need is some 'wisdom people' around you who will help you reflect honestly, and who won't fall into the same panic you are in and try to fix you too quickly."

"Wisdom people?"

"People who are more than successful; they are wise. They've figured out how life works, they have made it through 'deep adulthood' and took great notes, and now are willing to share that knowledge. They're passed the foolish infatuations with power, prestige, and influence. Usually, they've been broken themselves. They know God's voice and live out of their center. They are out there. You just have to know where to find them."

"You're a 'wisdom person,' aren't you?" Brian asked quietly. Al sat back, flattered, but accepting.

"I feel pretty blessed to have found you," Brian finished.

Brian's heartfelt confession had created a mild awkwardness. Both men pulled back a bit and looked about, policing the room to see if there were any eavesdroppers.

They fell into an awkward silence having violated the unwritten male contract to avoid intimacy at all costs. Then Brian broke the silence. "Let me see if I can summarize what you have said today about the dominion principle." He took out a piece of hotel stationary and began to write:

*The Eight Laws of Dominion*

*1. God gives each of us dominion assignments.*

*2. We do not need to manipulate to get a better assignment.*

*3. Dominion assignments are seasonal.*

*4. We must respect the "property lines" of others' dominion.*

*5. We must not take dominion over assignments God has not given us.*

*6. When God calls us to expand our dominion we must step out in faith and obey.*

*7. We must not give away dominion carelessly.*

*8. Our hearts must be prepared for dominion.*

"I think you have it," Al said with a hearty smile, rising to his feet. "I don't know if we will make it out of here for church tomorrow morning. Maybe we can celebrate with our own service? I noticed a chapel on the first floor," Al said. "Care to join me?"

"Sounds good. See you bright and early."

# TEN

The two men met in the silent little chapel at 8:30 am. The empty chapel was peaceful, and the two men each prayed silently. After a time, Al took out his Bible, intending to read and teach some scripture in an attempt to put some sense of normalcy into this snow-bound Sunday.

Before he had a chance, the chapel door opened and in walked an older man holding a well-worn, brown leather Bible. "I'm sorry," the little man said, noticing Brian and Al in the front of the room. "I didn't think anyone would be in here. I thought I would sneak down here for some peace and quiet, and spend some time in the good book." He started to turn around when Al summoned him back. "Don't let us disturb you. We were just about to have a little Bible study but we could go somewhere else."

"No, please," said the man. "You were here first...What might you be studying this morning, if you don't mind my asking?" His accent was subtly British.

"I don't mind at all," replied Al. "We have been having a rather protracted discussion this weekend about being Christian in the business world."

"Downright impossible, I would say. One would have to..." The little man stopped in mid sentence. "I'm sorry," he continued, "you didn't ask my opinion," the old man said, apparently self-conscious of the tone and intention of his previous comment. "I am a minister, you see, well, a retired minister. The worst combination you might say. I'm an old man and a preacher, so not only do I have an opinion, but I feel I must broadcast it to everyone. Forgive my interruption."

Al looked at Brian. "You are welcome to join us, if you'd like."

"Well," said the old man. "If you're sure I'm not interrupting you. I'd love the company; I've been cooped up here since Thursday. Iron sharpens iron, they say. I must warn you, I'm a bit blunt, or so I've been told. But don't let my strong opinions unsettle you; I'm just an old man, an old man who thinks a lot of his own wisdom." He smiled and made himself at home in the chair next to Brian.

"I'm Al Hunter, this is Brian Tucker," Al said by way of introduction. "We attended the Builder Association's leadership seminar and well, got snowed in." They all shook hands.

"I'm Adrian Sinclair," the old man said. "As I said, I am a retired minister. This is a beautiful country you gentlemen have."

"Well, this isn't exactly our home. I'm from the Midwest and Brian is from Tennessee. Are you visiting the States?"

"No, I live in the States. I have lived a good part of my life here; don't let my accent fool you. I moved here with my parents after World War II, went to seminary here, pastored a few churches in New England, and spent the last 15 years in New York. I worked at a rescue mission in the heart of Harlem," Rev. Sinclair smiled.

"Good to have you, Reverend Sinclair. I look forward to your insight. Well, Reverend, Brian here has been struggling with a dilemma; it seems his pastor has offered him a position on staff at his church, but he's reluctant to give up his career.

There is no question that Brian loves God, and is willing to follow wherever God leads. But he is wondering whether the position at the church is a good fit for him, a better fit than his position at the construction company. And when I say fit, I am not strictly talking about personality, skills, desire, goals, and things of a more temporal nature. When I say fit, I mean spiritual fit. Is the pastoral position God's calling, or is the senior management position God's calling?" Al noticed that the Reverend was nodding his head. He looked anxious for a turn to give his opinion. "One of the conclusions we came to, was that the church can unintentionally diminish the spiritual importance of occupations outside 'full-time Christian service.' And during our discussion we wondered if a fresher biblical perspective might acknowledge work, whatever that may be, as an integral aspect of our partnership with God in expanding the Kingdom."

"I would be hesitant to fully endorse that position as authoritatively biblical," the Reverend said stiffly. Brian could tell that Al had been diplomatic to get his point across, and was hoping the Reverend would feel free to state his uninhibited opinion. Reverend Sinclair continued, "I think work can be good. There are disciplines and lessons we gain from work, whatever it may be, and certainly those help build the fortitude of the saints. But I have not seen in the Bible, or in my own experience, the spiritual benefit of work, especially in expanding God's kingdom. On the other hand, I have seen its destructive nature. Work, as we experience it now at the beginning of the 21st century, is not neutral in my opinion, and is certainly not harmless. Work, you see, cannot be separated from the system it supports, and I'm afraid that almost everything we call work, especially here in America, supports a system that I'm sure is quite contrary to the kingdom of God."

"But Reverend," Al spoke up. It was clear from his demeanor that he was not going to make a forceful effort to engage the Reverend with every opinion he had in his arsenal, but that he wanted to soften the Reverend's stance. "You can't believe that the clergy has a higher calling, than say, the doctor, or ambulance driver."

"This may sound a bit old-fashioned my friend, and I don't want the question to sidetrack your understanding of what I'm trying to say, but I do believe there is a higher calling. Not all clergy are responding to it, I concede. But my point is this. Again, it is a question of the system we support with our work. Capitalism is a relatively new system, a few hundred years old. This system consists of three basic elements; a market exchange, private property, and profit. Now I know it is not popular to criticize capitalism, but when you peel back the layers, the principles it is based on are 'dog-eat-dog.'" He stopped and looked up at Brian who appeared to him a little flushed from the tenor of his assault. "You will pardon me son. I don't mean to rain on your parade... I'm sure you carry yourself with utmost integrity, but I have spent many years on this earth working with the casualties of such a system. It has hardened my opinion that such a system is inherently heartless, voracious in its appetite to consume whatever it can." Brian nodded apologetically.

"But Reverend," Al interjected, "the incentives within capitalism, the freedom to be your own boss, to market your own idea, those incentives create the opportunities that, when realized, provide subsistence for whole communities; subsistence in the form of jobs, healthcare... Isn't that a miracle? That from one man's idea a community is employed, fed, sheltered, and valued?"

"I don't mean to offend you, but I find that to be a very naive understanding of entrepreneurialism. The entrepreneurialism I have seen has more often than not exploited the workers, manipulated the communities, and distorted the souls of those who rushed over others to be their own bosses. No, I'm afraid there is no miracle there. The problem is that fundamentally, capitalism is an immoral system." The Reverend noticed that Al was about to interject a point. He raised his hand to fend off the interruption. "Now, let me finish, young man. Even the founder of capitalism, Adam Smith, admitted this. I have preached many a sermon on the evils of capitalism and I can quote Mr. Smith in my sleep. This is how he described it:

> *"In spite of their natural selfishness and rapacity, though they mean only their own convenience, though the sole end which they proposed from the labours of all the thousands they employ, be the gratification of their own vain and insatiable desires...they are led by an invisible hand...and without intending it, without knowing it, advance the interest of society.*

"Greed is at the core of capitalism," the minister continued, accentuating the word 'greed.' "Greed is the love of money, and I am afraid it comes at a horrible cost for society. This is why we must not naively court this spiritual harlot. The Bible speaks very plainly on these matters. The prophets cry out against economic injustice. The epistles warn that the love of money is the root of all evil. And Jesus himself said that our status in heaven will depend on how we treat the poor."

Al withdrew his hand, realizing that the Reverend had ceased conversing and was now preaching.

"A system with such an evil foundation can only expect to bear evil fruit," he explained, looking steadily from Al to Brian and back. The Reverend continued for ten more minutes identifying in lurid detail the abuses of capitalism. He talked about the widening income gap between the rich and the poor, the exploitation of third-world workers, the sweatshops in Southeast Asia. His strongest words were for the political and business leaders. He pronounced woe on the book-cookers, the inside traders, the mutual fund-skimmers, the corrupt executives who, after destroying perfectly viable companies and bringing economic calamity to thousand of families, cut loose with golden-parachutes and floated off to Vail.

"Capitalism," he concluded, "has created a culture of greed, selfishness, and materialism in America. It has encouraged the worship of false idols, the idol of mammon, and created an entertainment industry that sells sex and violence because it pays. Capitalist political leaders, blinded by their infatuation with the greedy system, look the other way as corporations, and forgive my vulgarity here, but they look the other way as corporations 'rape' the planet." The Reverend paused, realizing he had invested an uncomfortable amount of passion in the subject. As if to justify his intensity, the Reverend continued. "I've lived with the victims of capitalism," he said, his voice breaking. "I've held the crack babies while they struggled to breathe. I carried a homeless man, frozen to death on the streets of Harlem, to the morgue. I've wept with welfare mothers who can't make ends meet on the $5.75 they make at Taco Bell. And all of this in the richest nation on earth! How can we justify this! How dare we pay our CEOs millions when we refuse our city workers a living wage?!" At this the Reverend fell into a coughing spasm. He loosened his tie as Brian jumped up to fetch a glass of water for the old man.

Brian was deeply affected by the Reverend's 'sermon.' Brian's need for answers took over and before he knew it, he had asked, "So what can we do?"

The Reverend looked over at Brian, regained his composure, as if to say, 'maybe it's not as bad as I paint it,' and said with a gentle voice, "Capitalism isn't going anywhere soon. It's the system we have to live in. But Jesus told us to be as wise as serpents and as gentle as doves as we pick our way through this corrupt world system. We are supposed to be in the world and not of it. This is how we should live: like Jesus. First, we must serve the poor. Volunteer. Get involved with a soup kitchen, a mentoring program, or meals on wheels. And if you are impassioned, write editorials and letters to your newspapers and congressmen, urging them to support policies that help the poor."

"Second, give, and give generously. We ought to be ashamed of our standard of living when there is so much suffering in the world, when so many need so much. Give especially to those causes that help the neediest." Another coughing fit caused him to take a large gulp of water. After he caught his breath, he concluded, "And finally, maybe it's time for you to deny yourself and take up your cross. If you have done well, if you have been rewarded by the system, then give back. If you have earned enough to live on, then retire early. Give your remaining years to something that matters for eternity. Invest in people, not corrupt dreams."

The Reverend stopped abruptly and looked at the two men. Their stark silence confirmed that he had overeagerly stated his case and perhaps had built a wall between him and his new acquaintances. "How embarrassing," he thought. What was left, he decided, was an awkward segue and then a quick escape. His gaze moved from the two gentlemen's faces to the front of the chapel, where a huge window boasted a majestic view of the mountainside. "Look," he said. "How peaceful it looks covered in snow." Al looked over at the scene and nodded, and Brian, his voice thin and nervous, offered, "Yes. How beautiful." Brian looked over at the Reverend. He saw how tired and embarrassed he looked. Aware of the tension he created the Reverend stiffened in his chair, bringing the focus back to the immediate circle of men and said, "Gentlemen, I have thoroughly enjoyed your company this morning, but I must go rest. I'm rather tired." He looked at Al and then Brian, lingering on Brian's discomfited face. "Forgive me if I have in any way forced my positions on you," he smiled apologetically. "Remember, gentlemen, I am an old man and a former preacher, as I said, the worst combination." Now he looked tired, drawn, and gaunt. Both Brian and Al became a little concerned.

"I'm sorry…" he finally said. "High blood pressure, you know. Doctor says I am paying for all the years I pushed my body to limit. I regret I am going to have to excuse myself and go lie down. Naps; I need a few a day, it seems. The consequence of old age, I'm afraid. Please excuse me."

As the Reverend moved toward the door, Al was convicted that parting in silence was a most ungracious conclusion to the morning's awkward exchange. Before he knew what he was saying, he turned and asked, "Reverend? If you are free this afternoon we would love to have you join us for coffee."

The Reverend turned around, bolstered by the obvious kindness Al had extended. "That is very kind of you," he said. "I thank you for the offer. If you don't mind I will delay my response until I have rested and know if I feel up to it, but thank you." The Reverend shuffled toward the door of the chapel, his step a little more sluggish than when he arrived.

This morning Brian had looked confident, steadfast, almost anxious in his quest to face his dilemma, but now he look confused.

"Excuse me, Al," Brian said abruptly. "I need to check my e-mail."

Brian hurried from the room.

# ELEVEN

Brian tossed his Bible on the chair in his hotel room and fell onto the king-sized bed. Reverend Sinclair's passionate remarks had pierced him. The fiery little Brit had stoked the coals of guilt Brian had been trying to douse for years. He felt angry at Al, even betrayed. How could he be so gullible? Why had he been so quick to open his heart to the man, so easily persuaded that what he said was true? Brian's own father had died when he was twelve, leaving a hole in his soul that Brian had often looked to older men to fill. Sometimes, he needed a father figure too much. Had it happened again? Brian began to comprehend the profound spiritual crossroads he was facing. God had called him to leave everything for the ministry, just as the early disciples had done. Of course he loved his job – didn't the disciples love theirs? Hasn't God always called men and women to leave the comforts of the world and forsake all in following Jesus? He'd been looking for a way to rationalize his way out of obeying the clear call of God through his pastor. Al had been the perfect accomplice in this plan.

Brian booted up his laptop, connected with the internet, and clicked on his e-mail icon. He scrolled through his address book, found his pastor's name, and started to tap out an e-mail informing his pastor that he was ready to accept the staff position. A blinking icon at the bottom of his screen informed Brian that several new e-mails had come in over the day. Brian clicked on his inbox and scanned the new list. Two e-mails were from his travel agent about Monday flights out of Denver. Three others were spam. The remaining e-mail was from Ashley Brandeis, a friend he'd met at Auburn years ago, and then again after his divorce, had reconnected with through the singles group at his church. They had dated somewhat seriously before Ashley moved to Portland, and had remained friends via e-mail ever since. Brian often regretted not pursuing Ashley more intentionally. She was a vivacious, bright, articulate young woman who needed three lifetimes to fulfill all her dreams. Ashley had gone on staff with a campus Christian organization after Auburn and had done well. She then returned to school for an M.B.A., and upon completion, had taken a job with a start-up pharmaceutical company in Portland two years ago. Receiving Ashley's e-mail reminded Brian how much he missed her.

> *To: brian-tucker@vanguardconstruction.com*
> *From: BrandeisAshley@aol.com*
>
> *Greetings from rainy Portland! It's still beautiful here, though, and when the sun does shine you sure appreciate it. For some reason I have been thinking a lot about you this weekend, Brian. Are you O.K.?*
>
> *I'm better than O.K. Do you remember how much I enjoyed my work with students when I was in campus ministry? I think I told you when I went back to school for my M.B.A., that I wondered if I'd ever find anything as fulfilling as campus ministry. Those were some of the best years of my life. I thank God for them.*

*And you know what? I thank God for this crazy company I'm working for now. I have a lot of respect for Dr. Cruise, our founder and CEO. He cares about profit but he cares about people, too. He holds a patent on an Alzheimer's drug that could help a lot of people when the FDA gives us the green light. He's created a corporate culture here that is, well, I know this sounds odd, but spiritual. I don't mean that we have Bible studies all day long. I mean I have this keen sense that God is in what we are doing, pleased with what we are doing, partnering with us in our work.*

*I dreaded leaving everyone, and especially you, Brian, (did I say that? Well, it's the way I feel so I said it anyway). But I've really not been lonely. The marketing team I work with has really become close. We've gone through so much together trying to bring new products to market. Most of us are single, so we hang out a lot after work. Our softball team whooped a bunch of cocky software programmers from Microsoft® last spring! Most of us commute so we aren't as involved with relationships in our neighborhoods as we'd like to be — work is kind of our neighborhood. A few of us get together on Friday mornings to pray, look at scripture, and talk about our lives.*

*It's great to earn a paycheck, too. I still believe in supporting people for "full-time ministry" (what a lousy term, but at least you know what I mean). But it feels right somehow to receive a salary for my work. Dr. Cruise calls this "economic viability." It's one of his main talking points. Portland, as you know, has had a depressed economy since the timber industry went under in the eighties. Unemployment here is the highest in the nation. Our little company (not so little anymore) hired twenty people last year. If we keep growing like we are, we'll hire forty next year. Lots of these folks are highly skilled but just cannot find work. In his "state of the business" talk Dr. Cruise pointed to that as one of our greatest accomplishments — allowing people to become economic producers instead of consumers.*

*And it is not just highly skilled workers Dr. Cruise cares about. He put our warehouse downtown in a part of town that most businesses ignore. The neighborhood is a bit run-down and doesn't have a great labor pool. Dr. Cruise created a jobs training school in the community, and now he trains unskilled workers and hires them for the warehouse. Two other companies have joined us downtown. So many new employees are coming into the area that a new gas station, a convenience store, and a McDonalds have opened up. We feel that the whole neighborhood is starting to turn around.*

*Did I mention that Dr. Cruise is from Brazil? After a trip down there a year ago he came back all worked up about poverty in Latin America. And do you know what he's working on next? He wants to start a pharmaceutical company in Brazil! Says that a good business can really serve a country — bring jobs, make people economically viable. I'm supposed to help him train the marketing team.*

*One of the biggest surprises has been how natural and easy it is for me to share my faith here.*

*When I was in campus ministry, I had to work so hard to "break in" to the student's world. They often seemed suspicious of me, wondered why I was there. Here, spirituality is just one of the many things we naturally talk about. I've learned to be winsome about it – I listen a lot more than I talk, and when I do talk about my spiritual life, I try to do so in a way that respects their own journey, even learn from their journey.*

*This e-mail is getting too long, but there is one more thing I like about my work here – I'm having fun! Don't misread me; there are lots of problems and plenty of bad days. (I'm writing this at a coffee house and have had a bit too much caffeine. Maybe that is why I feel so positive today!) But at the end of most days, even most weeks, I feel good. It's fun to work hard, be a part of a team, develop a product that helps others, and make a good living at the same time.*

*Brian, you have been on my mind a lot lately, especially this weekend. It may be that I miss you more than I thought I would. (We sure do say things in e-mails we'd never say in person, don't we?) But there is something else going on as well. I have this sense, this gut feeling or impression, that you are at a crossroads, and that God is inviting you to see things with new eyes. I always get nervous when God gives me this stuff for people. I almost didn't share it with you; this seems so vague and we haven't talked in a month. Do with it what you want.*

*Love,*
*Ashley.*

Brian scrolled to the top of the e-mail and read it again, then deleted his half-written e-mail to his pastor. Ashley had a powerful way of speaking into his life. Maybe that is why he missed her friendship so much. But what did these words mean? The timing was uncanny. Ashley had a knack for that, too. It was as if God tapped her on the shoulder at times and whispered, 'take this message to Brian for me please.' Brian felt vulnerable, yet strangely cared for. For a man who normally didn't feel too much, he was overwhelmed with a dizzying array of emotions – rekindled affection for Ashley, love for his pastor, and ironically a warm fondness for both Al and Reverend Sinclair, blended with confusion and even fear. His anger towards Al had dwindled considerably since the awkward discussion in the chapel. Reverend Sinclair's passionate mini-sermon about the evils of commerce had sent him reeling. He had a troubling tendency, born out of a sincere desire to please God, to overreact to passionate spiritual arguments and to act before reflecting on them. Now he felt less certain that he agreed with the elderly gentleman. And what about Ashley's words? Wasn't he at a crossroads? Hadn't Al been helping him to see with new eyes?

Brian forwarded Ashley's e-mail to Al and wrote him a brief note.

> To: *alhunt@venturecap.com*
> Fr: *brian-tucker@vanguardconstruction.com*
> Re: *Apology and request*
>
> *Sorry for the way I left so abruptly this morning. What Reverend Sinclair said made a lot of sense to me. He raised many of the doubts I've had myself. Yet what you have been saying has made a lot of sense, too. Anyway, sorry. When I got back to the room I opened an e-mail from a friend. I'm learning to pay attention to the timing of*

*things, like being here this weekend with you! This e-mail, as you will see, has a unique timing to it as well. It's a little personal, but I'd like you to read it and talk about it with me. Could we take a walk after lunch? I think the snow has stopped for now.*

    *Brian*

# TWELVE

Crews with snow blowers had cleared the resort's sidewalks, which led to the main road; now open thanks to the pre-dawn work of snowplows.

"I take it you got my e-mail?" Brian asked, a little awkwardly, as he and Al headed down the sidewalk towards the main road.

"I did," Al answered a little crisply. "What was going on there? Why did you leave so quickly?"

Brian explained how confused he'd felt after Reverend Sinclair's thoughts on commerce and how he feared his reluctance to go on staff on his church was a form of rebellion against God.

"Do you still feel that way?" Al asked, his voice warming.

"I'm not sure what to think," Brian replied. "I know serving on the staff of a church is a great calling."

"We both agree with that," Al affirmed.

"What I am still not convinced of is whether or not a life in business can be an equally valid calling."

Al thought for a moment, and then said, "You asked me Friday night to share with you how I've integrated my business life with my spiritual life. Three basic beliefs guide me. We've talked about the first one: I believe I have dominion. The second basic belief that guides me is this: I believe that commerce is good."

"I doubt Reverend Sinclair would agree with you," Brian remarked.

"I doubt he would, either." Al replied. "But your friend Ashley does."

"How do you know?"

"Because I read her e-mail," Al replied. "Do you remember when Ashley said she thanked God for her work?"

"Yes."

"She ought to. God created commerce. That's why it is good."

"So God created commerce? That makes Him a capitalist?" Brian joked.

"An entrepreneur at least," Al shot back. "Think about it. Do you remember the verse in Genesis we looked at yesterday that told human beings to be fruitful and multiply, fill the earth and subdue it, and have dominion over all the earth?"

"Yes," Brian answered.

"All the seeds of commerce are hidden in that command. God certainly foresaw us as farmers and shepherds; the basis for an agricultural economy was there nearly from the beginning. Commerce had to be foreseen as the basis to distribute resources, to share commodities. There was nothing corrupt about it. People began to trade cows for crops. Then money, coins, pebbles, whatever was instituted for convenience. Cows didn't fit very nicely in billfolds." Brian chuckled, feeling some of his peace return. Al continued, "Simple subsistence economies mushroomed into the complex economic system we live in today. God created human beings to be interdependent, to be connected. Commerce is an expression of that interdependence. I need a shirt and you make a shirt. You sell the shirt to me and we both win. You make a profit and I get a shirt. Besides that, we might even start a friendship."

"But what about all those verses in the Bible that condemn wealth?" Brian asked.

"This is where Reverend Sinclair and I see things differently," Al replied. "I believe the Bible condemns the abuse of money, the worship of money, not the making of money. Many texts actually applaud hard work that results in a profit. Proverbs 31, for example, talks about the ideal woman. Do you know what the writer praises her for?"

"I'm afraid I don't," Brian replied.

"He praises her for buying a field, making a profit, and investing her earnings in a vineyard. He praises her for being a good businesswoman."

The two men had reached the main road now and turned towards town.

"Ashley's found some great relationships at work, too," Al continued. "That's another reason why I believe commerce is good."

Seeing that Brian did not yet follow his argument, Al said, "Jesus boiled all of Christianity into two simple commandments. Do you remember what they are?"

"Sure," Brian replied with confidence. "Love God with all your heart, mind, and strength and love your neighbor as yourself."

"Okay. Without community, where is your neighbor?"

Brian returned an inquisitive frown, as if he'd just been tricked.

"Christ linked loving God and loving people in these commandments. That is the heart of Christianity. Commerce provides the perfect backdrop to accomplish this."

Brian was not yet convinced. "Commercial relationships still feel, I don't know, professional, exclusive maybe. It's hard to see them as 'holy,' or spiritually significant. I think of pastors listening to dark confessions, or missionaries helping poor people in impoverished countries build homes. Those are the relationships that inspire me when I think about God's work."

"Why so lofty? Biblical teachings are pretty down to earth," Al responded. "We are to be gentle, kind, humble, generous. If your commercial relationships are marked by these characteristics, then they are 'holy,' because the God who created that relationship is holy. Commerce is the classroom where we learn to live and love in community."

Brain still felt disconnected, still defensive as he clung to his idealized understanding of holiness.

"How many names do you have in your Palm?" Al asked.

"Dozens, hundreds maybe," Brian responded.

"That's your community. That's where you live out the two greatest commandments," Al pointed out.

Brian was mute, unable to access his opinion.

Al continued, "As business people we are always building relationships - look at all the associations and societies we develop. Do those associations exist only to make the commercial enterprise function more effectively? Is the only satisfaction we receive in commercial relationships monetary? That is a very cynical understanding of commerce."

Brian nodded, as if he were being challenged to let go of that type of cynicism.

"Commerce causes more human conversations, more interrelation, more activity, and more opportunity to know other people than any other system. And that is not bad, it is good."

Al and Brian walked together silently for a while, savoring the rare quiet of a snow-muffled Colorado valley. Then Al said, "Ashley's boss, Dr. Cruise, was it? He spoke about economic viability. That is another reason why I believe commerce is good. Commerce makes people economically viable."

Brian's resistance was slowly starting to thaw.

"Have you ever heard of George Mueller?" Al asked.

"No." Brian said. "You keep exposing my shallow knowledge of history."

"Well, George Mueller ran a 19th century orphanage. Mueller became famous for the way he funded his orphanage," Al explained. "He decided never to ask for money. He wouldn't even make his needs known to his friends. Whenever the orphanage was about to run out of money, George Mueller got the kids together and they prayed. Each time God miraculously provided money to keep the orphanage going."

"God is good," Brian said.

"Yes, God is good, but that story could mislead Christians into foolishly rejecting other ways God provides," Al replied. "I'm afraid that stories like Mr. Mueller's mixed in with a good dose of dualism have led many Christians to misunderstand how God normally provides for people."

Al paused, and then said, "Let me put it this way. Suppose Mr. Mueller had run low on money in his orphanage. And suppose he prayerfully decides that the orphans are going to start a shoe repair business. They put out their shingle and within days are making a steady stream of income, enough to pay their rent, buy groceries, and even give some away to the other orphanage down the street. My bet is that if Mr. Mueller had raised money that way, no one would have ever written about him and he wouldn't be the spiritual hero he is today."

"I don't mean to get stuck on this, but praying and seeing God do miracles feels better than the commercial way."

"It may feel better, but it's not!" Al answered. "Look at 1 Thessalonians 4:11. 'Work with your hands...so you will not be dependent on anybody.' And Proverbs 10:4 'A slack hand causes poverty, but the hands of the diligent makes rich.' Brian," Al continued, "I believe that nothing is better for a person than to work hard at a job they love and earn a decent living in the process. Commerce gives people a chance to be economically viable. I encourage the companies I work with to make one of their corporate goals finding good people and 'infrastructuring' them to be economically viable."

"But not everyone fits in the category of 'good people' who are ready to be 'infrastructured,'" Brian protested. "What about the poor?"

"Is your friend Ashley helping the poor?" Al asked.

"Not really, no," Brian responded. "She used to volunteer at a homeless shelter – we used to do it together — but I don't think she helps the poor anymore."

"Did you read the same e-mail I did?" Al asked pointedly.

"Yes. But I didn't read much about a homeless ministry in it," Brian shot back.

"You'd do well to heed your friend's advice and start seeing with new eyes," Al responded tartly. "What about the warehouse her company has built downtown? What about the business they are starting in Brazil? What about the jobs training school? Isn't that 'helping the poor' – by helping them to learn job skills and creating businesses that create jobs?"

Both men walked in silence. Their conversation had gained an uncomfortable edge to it. Finally Al said more gently, "Brian, there was a season in my life when I gave a lot of hours to hands-on service to the poor. It was rewarding and meaningful. I still do some volunteer work. And if it is the burden of your heart and you are equipped, volunteerism is wonderful; it is like the eagle and the wind. What I realized

was that I am good at starting businesses. I came to the conclusion that the best way to serve the poor in my community
is to create jobs. When I first started to understand the power
of this, I wondered how it applied to my giving. I wanted to
be generous, but what was the most strategic way to use the
money I had to give? That's one reason why I started the venture capital business. I figured using my extra financial
resources to create new businesses was a very strategic way to
leverage my money and serve the most people."

"Do you give charitably?" Brian asked.

"Of course I do. I tithe, I make donations very thoughtfully. We have many opportunities to give money away and we
should soberly take them; tithing, supporting charities and
causes, lending money to people struggling...My work as a
venture capitalist is my way of shalom-making. I spread the
peace of God through funding opportunities that create economic viability for people."

Brian smiled feeling surprisingly supportive of the direc-
tion the conversation was taking. "I read a Wall Street Journal
article once where a writer argued that Bill Gates helped more
people than Mother Theresa ever did. He identified the tech-
nology he developed, the jobs he created, and the billions he's
given away as support for his argument."

"I don't think pitting people against each other in such
a contest is very fair, but I agree that we probably don't give
Bill Gates enough credit for creating economic viability for
hundreds of thousands of people." Al paused, feeling more
confident that Brian was seeing the issue with an eye toward
a further horizon.

"I haven't even cited the most obvious example in
Ashley's e-mail that proves that commerce is good," Al added.

"Which example is that?"

"Her comments about how easy and natural it is to have spiritual discussions at work," Al replied. "Commerce is good because it is a wonderful place to share your spiritual story and help people fall in love with Jesus Christ. We moderns sometimes fail to appreciate the historical actualities that God used to spread his Word. And believe me, his Word spread like wildfire in the early centuries of the church. The early Church grew at an alarming rate, an average of 40% a decade through several hundred years. And all with no Promise Keepers, no seminaries, no 'full time Christian ministers'…" Brian detected a bit of angst at the tail of Al's statement.

"Ironic isn't it? They had none of the 'institutional' support that we have, yet their numbers increased, and ours, today, decrease. They used commerce to move them and their faith; we try to keep our faith centrally located, in the walls of the church."

"Are you familiar with Lydia in the New Testament?" Al asked.

"I know she was a convert, that's about it," Brian said

"She was a good friend of Paul's that he met on a missionary journey. She converted and helped establish a church at Philippi. Do you know what she did, her occupation?" Brian shook his head. "She sold fabric that had been dyed. And Paul happened to be a tent maker. Is it at all possible that their initial contact may have been commercial? Now realize I am only hypothesizing, but isn't it possible?"

Brian was fascinated by the depth of Al's biblical knowledge.

"When we allowed our faith to be pulled out of our work, we lost the normal way the gospel has always spread. We started to see evangelism and discipleship as 'spiritual activities' that take place before or after work."

"Go on," Brian said.

"The early church didn't divide the world in half like that. They often lived where they worked, for example. A typical family would have a shop on the first floor and live on the second floor. Home churches met in businesses. And they talked about the gospel in their businesses as well. Relationships nurtured through commerce were the normal paths on which the gospel traveled."

Al stopped, knowing that he had given Brian quite a load to digest. He let a few moments of silence pass, and then spoke quietly, "God created commerce for us, and for Himself, and you know what? I think He enjoys it. I think He enjoys when people at the Haymarket in Boston bring fresh fish and fresh vegetables and haggle and laugh as they trade. It is fun. Maybe that is the final treasure God has packed into commerce; it is fun."

"Ashley mentioned that, too," Brian pointed out. "She said she's having a lot of fun."

The two men had made their way to the tiny mountain town that serviced skiers and hikers and the occasional restless visitor who wandered in from the resort.

"Buy you a soda?" Brian asked.

"Diet, if they have it," Al replied. Brian bought two colas and they sat on a bench in front of a ski-rental store.

"So the second belief you have about business is that commerce is good. Let me try to summarize your reasons. Brian pulled his Palm from his coat pocket and typed in:

*Why Commerce is Good*

*1. God created commerce.*

*2. Commerce creates community.*

*3. Commerce creates economic viability.*

*4. Commerce serves the poor.*

*5. Commerce provides a natural way for the gospel
to spread.*

*6. Commerce is fun.*

He read the list to Al.

"Couldn't have said it better myself," Al said. "I think I'm doing more kingdom work through commerce than I ever did as a priest."

Al's last remark seemed unnecessary, even mean-spirited to Brian. Al's comments about the organized church often had an edge to them, Brian noticed. Brian sometimes had an unusual ability to discern spiritual struggles buried beneath the surface of other people's lives. The insight came upon him almost spontaneously, a flash of inspiration that gave him supernatural insight into the inner workings of another person's life. Nine times out of ten his hunches where dead on. Brian sensed a struggle in Al, and felt his hunch was right.

# THIRTEEN

"Al, can I ask you a personal question?" Brian asked. Al did not respond immediately. He seemed surprise by Brian's question. It occurred to Brian that Al enjoyed the fatherly role and was less comfortable as a peer.

"It's not a question, really," Brian went on tentatively. "Sometimes I have this strange ability to see into people's souls. It's like I can see who they are supposed to be, and what keeps them from their destiny. It's almost like a supernatural insight. I'm feeling that way now."

"Well, what are you feeling?" Al asked.

"My sense is that you have some unresolved issues with the church. My gut is that it has something to do with the church where you served before going into business. I sense that God wants you to let some old hurt go so you can embrace your calling with more freedom and power," Brian paused. "I'm usually not wrong about these things," he added, beginning to smile.

"Smiling at my evident discomfort, are we?" Al asked. Then, "Brian, a lot of my thoughts and feelings are pretty raw. I've been living these ideas, but have never talked about them in such depth. I've been surprised at some of the feelings that have surfaced with some of the ideas. I'm not proud of that. The world doesn't need another angry reformer," Al said reflectively. "I do love and need the church. Forgive me for implying otherwise."

Al sat quietly, weighing Brian's words. "It's hard to tell who is mentoring whom here," Al finally said, pulling his journal from his coat pocket. "I want to share with you something I was writing in my journal right before we met Friday night. It is uncanny. This is what I was writing when our paths crossed." Al opened the journal, slid his reading glasses on, and very purposefully, with a hint of strain in his voice, began to read:

> *Heavenly Father,*
>
> *It's been a long time since I left the priest-hood. It's been quite an adventure and I've loved the path You've led me on. You have me in a place of reflection about my past and my future. I hope I have been faithful with my assignment so far, and I want to finish well. What is it You would have me do in this final season of my life? Lord, You said to the Father, "I have completed the work you gave me to do." I want to be able to say that, too.*
>
> *Something stops me, Lord. Something stands in the way of the peace I have felt when I have stood before You, blameless. What sin do I hold in my heart? I need You to know and I want to know.*
>
> *Is there still bitterness in me? I fear there is. During my workshop after I told them my back-ground, a few people started calling me 'Father Al.' I'm sure they were trying to be friendly, maybe reaching out, but the phrase hit me like a ton of bricks. I resented it, but just smiled. Is this my sin?*

Al's voice cracked. He quickly wiped a tear off his cheek and kept reading.

> *I fear I still carry my wound from the church. I encouraged the flock to be the wonderful creatures You had made them to be. I urged them to embrace their destinies, wherever that might lead them. Yet when it was my turn to embrace my own destiny, they turned away from me, some with hurtful bitterness.*
>
> *You know I have been faithful to press in to this wound. Please tell me I have made progress. Please tell me I am further down the path than I was the day I resigned, because sometimes, Lord, I don't feel that way at all. By faith I trust I have been faithful to forgive this.*
>
> *Father, maybe I am angry with You. Since You called Brother Bennett home, I have felt alone in this struggle. You allowed me to be transparent with him. I miss my spiritual director, and confess I feel the burden of carrying this alone, for I trust no other than him. I don't want to continue in this bitterness; it hurts, it's a dull ache, it's a cancer. Don't let it have me.*
>
> *Right now, before You, in my need, I confess I am scared. I want to be done with this bitterness. I want to forgive my old parishioners, my old church, my new church, myself. I cannot ask with any more honesty than I have right now - Lord, help me! Bring me a body to surround my healing. I need my wounds dressed. I need my broken body soothed. I do not want to continue with anger. How dare I withhold forgiveness when I have been forgiven so much?"*

*Al stopped, visibly moved with his own con-
fession. He looked up at Brian. "I'd just finished
writing that sentence when you walked in, Brian.
With your spiritual insight, you've confirmed the
unforgiveness I had hidden in my heart. Looks like
I have some unfinished business with the Father. . . ."*

Then, oddly, Al laughed, dried his eyes, and stood up.

"Now why are you laughing?" Brian asked, confused.

"Because I'm catching on to what God is up to here."

"I'm glad you are. You'll have to fill me in," Brian said, masking frustration.

"He's not letting me play the role of wise sage, Brian, where I dole out principles from on high and leave you in awe of my wisdom. He's making me live out my beliefs right here before your eyes."

"And what belief are we living out at this moment, if you don't mind my asking?" Brian wondered.

"My third belief about business is this: It's about people. Business is the perfect arena to invest in people's lives, to help them fulfill their destiny, even to do deep soul work," Al explained. "That is what is happening here...at a business conference. We are doing some pretty heavy lifting here. You've managed to speak into an area of my life I've kept hidden from everyone but one man for nearly thirty years. And you did it at a business conference."

"It has been a very significant weekend for me, too," Brian admitted.

"And speaking of people," Al said, tossing his soft drink can into the garbage and wrapping a scarf around his neck, "I think we need to get back and check on Reverend Sinclair."

# FOURTEEN

"You're very fond of Ashley," Al observed as they walked back towards the hotel. Brian nodded.

"What is it you like about her?"

"Her eyes. Her hair. The way she laughs," Brian replied wistfully.

"I suspect there's more to her than good looks," Al probed.

"Ashley is, well..." Brian scanned the mountains rimming the valley as if the words he was looking for might fly over the treetops. "Ashley is... alive." Brian thought for a moment, then asked, "Have you ever heard that saying, 'Dead at thirty, buried at seventy?' A lot of people I know live that way. Ashley doesn't. She is fully alive."

"You could feel that in her e-mail," Al remarked. "How many people do you know who are fully alive?"

"Not many," Brian replied. "Work seems to suck the life out of most people. Work becomes a kind of prison they want to escape from."

"I know," Al agreed. "But I've found work to be a life-giving place. My work is my parish, the place where I invest in people, where I help them become fully alive." Even though it was only mid-afternoon, the sun slipped behind a mountain peak, casting the valley into shadow and dropping the temperature significantly. Brian and Al quickened their pace.

"A few months ago I was doing some exit interviews for a pharmaceutical company client," Al began. "Among the departing employees was a woman who had been with the company throughout her career. In fact, I had recommended her when she was coming straight out of college. She was one of those people who was going to go as far as she wanted: tremendous leadership skills, incredibly good with people, she had senior management written all over her. I was told that the company had been very impressed with Maria. She was a team builder, but also had the unique gift to maintain her authority while inviting intimacy with her staff. She'd often find co-workers opening up to her, coming to her for counsel. People loved working for her, and she endowed them with something special; many on her staff would become stars in their own right. She had a lot of integrity as she developed employees. She also developed employees with an impeccable moral fortitude, I thought. Her staff and senior managers talked about Maria in almost hushed, reverential ways; it almost was like a religious experience for some of them."

"A born leader is a beautiful thing to see; it's like the eagle with the wind," Brian interjected.

"Maria was an eagle," Al agreed. "We were able to speak of things of faith as well. Maria had a rather dramatic conversion about a year ago. Underneath her excellence she was questioning the meaningfulness of her life. To say her faith complemented her skills is an understatement; her faith downright deepened, matured, multiplied, how ever you want to say it, her faith purified the marvelous abilities she already had. " Al paused as two deer darted across the road and into a nearby thicket. "Anyway, as I was saying, I was absolutely shocked to see her on my list for exit interviews. I could not for the life of me understand why she would be leaving."

"Why was she leaving?"

"She was leaving so she could go into 'full-time Christian ministry' she said. She had become involved in a women's ministry at church and was planning on raising financial support so she could devote all her time to discipling women. I was dumbstruck. Here was this marvelous woman with a staff of about 15 people, mainly women, and she was leaving her career to spend time 'discipling' women. I told her, very directly, that she was already discipling women at her work, that her staff was being given the love of Christ, but she wouldn't listen. She said that the politics and purpose of this life felt too worldly, too insignificant compared to the thought of serving God. 'Life is short,' she said, and she wanted to spend time doing what mattered."

"Dualism," Brian uttered involuntarily.

"Good. You're right. She was struggling against dualism," Al said. "I couldn't make her see that she had a powerful, effective ministry at the pharmaceutical firm. Why do we always assume that if we are going to 'pour into people,' we have to do it after work, before work, or on the weekends? We are so blind to the incredible opportunity work gives us to build people. My companies have been the schools where I've practiced spiritual formation and discipleship. I lose that platform if I leave my business. Maria, I'm afraid, is going to lose perhaps the most powerful ministry opportunity she'll ever have, and she may never understand that. God was working through her at work."

Shadows now covered the valley floor. Brian thought again of his job offer from his pastor. "I think what attracts me to the position on staff at my church," he said in-between gulps of air as they began the ascent up the hill towards the hotel, "is the opportunity to spend all my time discipling people. Isn't the church where that happens? Doesn't Paul say in his letter to the Ephesians that God gives the church pastors in order to build up the body of Christ and help God's people mature?"

"Yes, Paul does say that in the fourth chapter of Ephesians," Al agreed. "When we get back to the hotel I'd like to look at that passage a bit more closely with you. I don't mean to devalue the good work pastors do in helping people grow personally and spiritually. I'm just saying that you can do that at work as well as anywhere else. Spiritual growth doesn't just take place at church."

"How do you do that without being preachy?" Brian asked.

"I don't hand out tracks or have a bumper sticker on my car, if that is what you mean. I look for what I call 'identity opportunities.'"

"What are 'identity opportunities'?" Brian probed.

"Crisis points that naturally happen in day-to-day work, when a person's identity issues rise to the surface. Most people exert a lot of effort to keep their deep feelings about themselves stuffed down. I try to create a safe place for people to relax and discover what lies under the surface. I recently had an identity opportunity with one of our managers. Tony had been passed over for a promotion and was furious. The fact is he is right where he needs to be in terms of his skills and his experience. The promotion would've meant more prestige, but it would've also been a disaster for him personally. He came into my office when he found out he had been passed over — my door is usually open. Tony's on a spiritual journey himself, so I felt free to frame our discussion in those terms," Al qualified. "When he got through ranting about the injustice of it all, I asked him what hurt the most about being passed over. He was quiet for a while. He settled down a bit and quietly revealed that growing up he had an abusive father who constantly berated him, said he'd never amount to much. I was careful not to preach. I told him a little of my own story. I underscored some of the foolish things I did, things meant to court people's approval, things meant to satisfy my own sense of justice, things that in retrospect drained my soul more rapidly of peace and tranquility. I ended with how Jesus, in His faithfulness, was there for me to help me pick up the pieces."

Al looked over at Brian to see if he was tracking with him. "Then I told him that he was in the perfect place for his skills and gifts. It was hard because I knew he didn't want to hear it. I then told him I believed in him, I mentioned many of the skills and traits I admired in him. I told him I was proud of him and was thankful for everything he did for the company."

"Suppose Tony was in the wrong field, the wrong career. How would you tell him that?" Brian asked.

"Have you ever heard the term 'spiritual gifts'?'" Al asked Brian.

Brian nodded. Al continued, "The apostle Peter wrote, '*Each one should use whatever gift he has received to serve others.*' Does that just mean others in the church? I don't think so. The apostle Paul urged the Galatians to '*do good to all people.*' Back to my point, one of my most important jobs as a manager is to help my staff, people like Tony, identify their gifts and align them with the right task. Tony was living out of the 'oughts' – everyone around him thinks he *ought* to be in a more prestigious position. Loved ones can apply the worst kind of pressure this way. Tony's wife, and I know and love this lady like a little sister, so don't think I'm being overly critical, but she's a little spoiled. I love her and God bless her, but that's the truth. She thinks Tony *ought* to make more money, that Tony ought to have a more prestigious title. I'm there to help Tony discover his God-given nature, his spiritual gifts, and seek to develop those things instead of pursuing ideas other people have for him that may inhibit the development of those gifts, or distract him from living out of his nature. I'm there to help him see taking a position that doesn't fit his gifts or calling is a recipe for failure. In God's wisdom He made it difficult for us to go it alone." Al finished his sentence as they finally approached the hotel, then added, "I need to help Tony understand one more thing. Tony is an incredibly relational person. He loves people very well. He has a wonderful gift. In a very low-key, non-threatening way he is able to share his faith, his personal journey with Christ. This quality attracts people. You should see how people turn to him for help in their own spiritual pilgrimages. The ability to do this is a gift from God. If Tony had gotten that promotion, not only would he have found himself in water way over his head, he would've also found himself isolated from those who seek him for counsel. The promotion would have certainly made him less accessible, and probably would have dampened the vulnerability he naturally has that makes people feel safe sharing with him. I suspect he never considered that," Al said as they approached the front doors of the resort. The warm hotel lobby was a welcome refuge after an afternoon outdoors.

"I'm going to check on Reverend Sinclair," Al said. "Why don't we meet in the study at 9 o'clock and put a little closure on our weekend?"

# FIFTEEN

Brian glanced at his watch. It was a quarter past nine and no Al. Brian was enjoying the peace of the study, the warmth of the fire, and the taste of his Egyptian Licorice tea. He wanted to see Al and hoped that he would show up, but was content to just relax and stoke the fire. He looked up as the study door opened.

"I'm sorry I'm late," Al apologized, looking a little winded.

"No problem. I was just enjoying the fire," Brian said. He noticed that Al seemed much more relaxed, more at ease than he had been earlier in the day. "Have a seat."

The two men sat quietly, gazing into the fire.

"You are an answer to prayer, Brian. You are part of the body God is using to 'dress my wound,' to soothe my anger. Brian, you served a prophetic role in my life this weekend," Al clarified.

"Prophetic?"

"Yes. You functioned as a prophet."

Brian looked puzzled, but he also trusted Al's deep understanding of scripture. Al noticed his frown and said, "Let me explain. Prophecy is a very misunderstood gift. Let me return to the Ephesians passage you mentioned on our

walk this afternoon." Al took his Bible and his reading glasses from the inside pocket of his sports jacket. He cleared his
throat, "Paul says that Jesus gave *'some to be apostles, some to be
prophets, some to be evangelists, and some to be pastors and teachers
to prepare God's people for works of service, so that the body of Christ
may be built up.'*

"We are the body," Brian said.

"Yes, we are the body. It isn't a building, or an organization, it is us," Al replied. "Those gifts are for the church
body we worship with on Sunday, but they are also for two
brothers in Christ to minister to each other on snowed-in
weekends in Colorado. Paul's letter is addressed to 'the saints
in Ephesus.' The believers in Ephesus would have been scattered across the city. They gathered for worship in their
homes, which often doubled as their shops and businesses.
The line between the church and the marketplace was a lot
fuzzier for them than it is for us."

"But how do you mean that I was a prophet to you this
weekend? Don't prophets see future events?"

"As I said, I think it is a very misunderstood ministry.
Paul mentions five gifts in this passage; apostles, prophets,
evangelists, pastors, and teachers. These gifts all function in
the body today just as they did then, to build up God's people, to build up God's church. These aren't merely job
descriptions of what you need to start a church, in fact, the
early local churches, or house churches, probably didn't each
have these ministries. Yet these ministries functioned to build
the church. I would suspect that often believers with these different ministries ministered to each other in the market place."

"I don't see how these gifts work outside a church set-
ting. How does one preach or give prophecy outside the
church?"

"Brian, you ministered to me prophetically this afternoon, even though you didn't know it. Ashley ministered prophetically to you through her e-mail. A prophet is given supernatural insight into a person, and he shares that insight in a way that builds up, encourages, and calls out destiny. God gave you discernment into my struggle, the very struggle I was praying about when you walked in Friday night."

"I guess I always thought that a word of prophecy could only be given in a church service or a small group."

"Those are wonderful places for the prophetic gift to be used. But you are still thinking dualistically. Prophets can also minister prophetically *while they are doing business*, just like you ministered to me."

"Ours may not be the best example, as we were talking of 'spiritual things,' but I'm willing to bet," Al continued, "that you often speak prophetically into the people you work with. You have the God-given ability to see what a person can be, not just who they are, and call them towards that vision. Am I far from the mark?"

Brian felt a little flushed. He could recall many times when he spoke as he had spoken to Al tonight. He believed he had a God-given gift, or talent, but never understood it to be "prophetic."

"Prophets in the workplace call out destiny in a person," Al continued. "They encourage us to take dominion boldly, or warn us of taking dominion too lightly. They speak into our hearts and help us prepare our hearts for dominion. They clarify vision. We need them. Your company does not know how truly blessed they are to have you."

"You mentioned Apostles as a gift still functioning today. How so?" Brian asked.

"Apostles in the Bible were spiritual entrepreneurs, extending dominion into new territory, birthing new churches, stirring things up. Many of today's apostles start new churches or serve as missionaries, but some give birth to kingdom businesses. An apostle will see opportunities and create businesses that respond to the opportunity. An apostle is always breaking new ground for the kingdom." Al paused. As long as they were disclosing so intimately, he volunteered, "I think I have an apostolic gift. I love to find new ways to establish God's dominion through business. That's why I formed the venture capital company. It gives me a channel for my gifting."

"Okay, I can see the role of prophets and apostles in the business world," Brian allowed. "But give me an example of an evangelist in the work place."

"Do you remember Tony, the guy who was so frustrated because he was looked over for a promotion?" Al asked. "He's an evangelist."

"I think of Billy Graham when I think of an evangelist, someone presenting the gospel to thousands," Brian admitted.

"Tony presents the gospel in no uncertain terms," Al replied. "If you could see him you'd understand. Tony is a meek and humble man. People are attracted to him and love to be around him. Even people who don't necessarily like to hear about religion can take it when he gives a very practical example of faith in action. He presents the gospel with his life."

"And what about pastors?"

"Reverend Sinclair is a pastor, a shepherd," Al said. "Most of your good managers have pastoral gifts. They know how to walk with people and keep an eye on someone's growth. Reverend Sinclair told me that he is volunteering his time with a local foundation, spending half his week coming alongside men and women who are out in the marketplace. Pastors are shepherds, coaches, mentors, counselors. He's very good at it."

"But he seemed so anti-business!"

"Ironic, isn't it? It's odd because I would say he has a distaste for businesses, but he has a deep love for the business people."

"You were talking with him before we met tonight, weren't you?" Brian asked. "That is why you were late."

"I was," Al responded. "When I went to visit him this afternoon, I only planned on staying for a few minutes. I wound up staying two hours. He is a lot gentler than he appeared during our discussions today. He's very wise, very thoughtful; he knows how to pull out the deep thorns that pierce our hearts. I just went to check on him, and soon we were sharing our stories, much like you and I have. I told him about what I was writing in my journal. He listened well, and led me to some profound conclusions about my struggle with my past. Given how much we disagreed theologically on the nature of business, I never dreamed I'd go there with him. But I'm glad I did. I was late tonight because he insisted I return to his room this evening and let him pray for me. He is a prayer warrior." Al paused, "God used both of you this weekend. I prayed for people to help me resolve my anger towards the church. He sent me a pastor and a prophet."

"At a business seminar," Brian pointed out. Both Brian and Al laughed.

"Reverend Sinclair's gift is pastoring?" Brian asked.

"Yes, I would say so."

"Explain the teaching gift, then," Brian asked.

"I think it is time we rethought the role of teachers in the church," Al replied. "We tend to think of a teacher as someone who teaches the Bible to Christians in church. That's only one application of the gift. There is an important role for teachers in the business world. So much Christian teaching, as we practice it today, does not relate to the real world of work. We teach about Abraham, or the epistles, but outside of the context of the Bible we forget to teach Christian principles for people to use when negotiating contracts, or recruiting employees. I try to give my staff a greater understanding of our role as businesspeople in establishing dominion. The preparation of young leaders, the deep personal work to prepare their hearts and minds for the responsibility for expanding dominion, calls for invested teachers right now. We may not need any more Captains of industry grooming young men to sail ruthlessly over the seas of commerce, but we do need humble mentors to cultivate character, and wise spiritual directors who will listen and guide according to the Spirit. There is a whole generation of capable young men and women who will die on the vine without willing spiritual fathers and mothers to speak into their lives. How will this new generation know how to create loving communities, honor 'property lines,' handle ethical dilemmas, draw out from under the broken shards of false identity true and integrated leaders? Who will teach them to apply their spiritual gifts vocationally? We need teachers who can weather tough lessons without the kind of trite answers you find in fill-in-the-blank discipleship books."

"Where do we start?"

"A few people already have. I know of a company that hired a retired seminary professor to come in and teach ethics, spiritual discipline, and contemplation. The seminary professor loved it; it forced him to go back to the scriptures with a whole new set of questions. The company loved it; even the non-religious folk enjoyed hearing a defense of ethics and sound business practices."

Al set his Bible aside, put his feet up on the hearth, and settled deeper into the oversized chair. Brian stretched his neck and straightened his legs making himself momentarily stiff as a board in the leather chair. "I've been thinking," Al said. "I hope my counsel hasn't been overly prejudiced by my own disappointments. I hope somewhere in our conversation you found something useful to take home and help you make your decision. This was a divine appointment, and I hope you have heard what God is trying to tell you. You have an important decision to make when you return home. Talk to your pastor. I want to be completely clear about what I have said: the church needs pastors, apostles, and prophets, but so does the business world, and when you walk outside the doors of the former you can invest yourself, with all your gifts, in the latter. Establishing dominion takes both the church pastor and the businessman. Both need to be men of God, discerning, humble, wise, and accountable. Whatever choice you make, don't stop expanding the kingdom of God, and know that God will go with you if you choose to remain a builder. He will bless your work if you ask Him."

"I think I've come to that same conclusion myself," Brian responded, rubbing his eyes.

"You have worn me out, my friend," Al said with a yawn. "I've said more than I should and that was hours ago. I don't have another profound word left in me." Brian closed his eyes. "And I don't have another profound question." The intensity gave way to lethargy as both men struggled to find the energy to leave. "Well, maybe I do have one question, Al."

Al groaned and pulled his forearm over his face. "And you can't e-mail it to me when you get back to Tennessee?"

"No, I'm serious. One more question."

"Shoot."

"Would you be my spiritual director?"

Al pulled his arm down and straightened up in his chair, a smile breaking over his tired face. "Well," the question had taken him a little off guard. "Yes, I'd be honored to, Brian. You get what you see, though, weakness, struggles, and all. So if that's okay with you, it's okay with me. It will be thoroughly enjoyable to continue this conversation." Al felt satisfied, happy. "Now, turnabout's fair play. I have one more question for you."

"Go ahead."

"Have you decided whether or not you are going to go on staff at your church?"

"Yes," Brian said, a weary smile spreading across his face. "I have."

# *The Family Business*

# ABOUT THE AUTHORS

**Steve Hall** is the president of Empire Corporation, a general contracting business in 18 states and $40 million in annual sales. Steve began Empire in 1979 with his wife Kathryn's $500 line of credit and little else. He'd sit in his empty office in the morning, call potential clients and say, "You are in luck. We have an opening. If you go with us today we can fit you in." In his late forties with dark hair, broad shoulders and a deep laugh, Steve is intense, passionate and bold.

Empire Corp tripled in size in 2003 and Steve found himself running out of lunches to explain his vision to workers, clients and interested friends. Steve invited Jeff Fray, John Secrest and Doug Banister to a retreat in August, 2003 where they wrestled with dualism and hammered out the three beliefs Al shares with Brian in this book. Jeff, John and Doug then taught through these materials in a Monday morning study at Empire Corporation in the fall of 2003. Sensing that these studies on faith and business might serve a broader audience, Steve asked for these concepts to be written down in a book.

**John Secrest** is one of the most respected missionaries in his denomination. He moved his young family to Budapest, Hungary in the mid-nineties, learned one of the world's most difficult languages with amazing speed and planted a thriving, Hungarian-speaking church. Today a native Hungarian pastors the church. John, in his early forties, has worked himself out of a job.

Since John has returned to the states, numerous churches have called him to be their pastor. But John, who has spent his entire professional life working for churches or missionary agencies, wants to pastor through business. With close-cropped hair, an engaging, confident smile and penetrating eyes, he looks more like a Navy Seal than a missionary. Presently John's role in the family business is buying and managing apartment complexes and launching a trade school to help construction entrepreneurs. Both John and Steve look forward to starting "kingdom businesses" in Eastern Europe as a way of extending God's loving dominion and spreading shalom in a broken part of the world.

**Jeff Fray** grew up a missionary kid in rural Sessame, Zimbabwe, a village so far in the bush that lions roared at night and elephants were a real threat. Jeff earned his PhD in psychology from the University of Tennessee and over ten years build a thriving group practice in Knoxville. Mid-life rumblings led Jeff into a relationship with a spiritual director, a journey that led to deep, personal transformation. The old wineskin was a poor fit for this new wine, and in 1999 Jeff, his wife Gail, and their three sons pulled up all their stakes and set off on an 18-month sailing adventure from Florida to Venezuela. Today, Jeff is living out his passion to be in the people-building business. He serves Empire Construction as the People Officer on the Board of Directors, he is a consultant/advisor to the WinShape Foundation of Chick-fil-A, and continues a part-time counseling/consulting practice.

**Doug Banister** is a writer, pastor and teacher. Doug, in his early forties, served as senior pastor of Fellowship Church for 15 years and is the author of two books: The Word and Power Church and Sacred Quest. A third book, The Community of Faith will be in bookstores in January of 2005. Doug has degrees from Northwestern University, Talbot School of Theology, and Gordon-Conwell Divinity School. He is presently pursuing a PhD in history at the University of Tennessee.

Doug thanks John, Jeff and Steve for inviting him to join them in this project. He also thanks:

Gail Fray for superb technical editing;

Jeff Townsend for helping shape the story and characters;

Bill Webb for explaining the world of a construction manager;

Joe Key, for his recommendation of Henri Nouwen's insights preparing your heart for dominion;

The Monday morning Empire group for their creative, challenging comments and suggestions;

The Friday lunch and breakfast groups for their blunt, insightful and sometimes even encouraging feedback.

This was a team project.